JESUS
SU
WORDS
& MUSIC
PRAISE
A SONGBOOK FOR ALL OCCASIONS

SU

First published 1982
Reprinted 1983, 1984

Compiled by **Norman Warren, David Peacock**
Words arranged by **Michael Perry**
Musical notation checked by **Noel Tredinnick**
Edited by **Simon Jenkins**

ISBN 0 85421 956 0

Scripture Union, 130 City Road, London EC1V 2NJ

Cover photograph: British Tourist Authority

Music Process and Typesetting by
Halstan & Co. Ltd., Amersham, Bucks., England.

Printed and bound in Great Britain
at The Pitman Press, Bath

ACKNOWLEDGEMENTS

This book had its origins in the Youth Praise committee, and many members of that original committee have given much encouragement and valuable advice on the contents of this present book.

We are particularly grateful to Michael Perry for checking all the words and punctuation, to Jean Dean for typing and retyping the words and sending out endless letters, and to Angela Reith for checking, and in many cases adding, the guitar chords.

We thankfully acknowledge the continued help and guidance of our printers. Finally a special thank you to my wife Yvonne, who has had to put up with bits of music lying all over the house for the best part of two years.

Norman Warren

INTRODUCTION

Revival in the church has invariably gone hand in hand with musical expression. Hymns, songs, and the shorter, simpler chorus have been pouring out over the past decade. Dozens of song books have been produced all over the world. Why then another?

In order to have a good variety of songs and choruses it has often been necessary to have a caseful of books. The aim of **Jesus Praise** has been to gather in one book a wide selection of those songs and choruses that have proved their worth over the past years. As well as this, a third of the book contains new and unpublished material.

There is a variety of styles, from four-part arrangements for a choir, to country and western songs. Most items have been arranged so that they can be readily played on the organ as well as the piano. In the main we have kept to the simpler keys, and in all items guitar chords have been provided. A number of the songs have new descants specially written for this book.

Jesus Praise is intended as a replacement for the enormously popular **Youth Praise** books – but it has a wider appeal. It is a book not only for young people, but also adults. It is an all-age Christian songbook. **Jesus Praise** should meet a widely-expressed need for a book of songs and choruses that can be used in public worship, at prayer meetings, in home groups, in youth groups and at family prayers.

The book contains a Scripture Index, so that those who are leading worship will be able to use choruses that relate directly to biblical themes and passages.

All possible effort has been made to trace copyright owners – which is no easy task when many well-known songs have become part and parcel of the life of the average church. Any errors or omissions will gladly be put right at the first opportunity.

It is our hope and prayer that public and home worship will be enriched through this book.

Norman Warren, David Peacock

And I heard every creature in heaven, on earth, in the world below and in the sea – all living creatures in the universe – and they were singing:

To him who sits on the throne and to the Lamb
be praise and honour, glory and might, for ever and ever.

Revelation 5:13

CONTENTS

Praise and Thanksgiving ... 1
The Father ... 54
The Lord Jesus Christ ... 65
The Holy Spirit ... 122
Fellowship and the Church ... 132
Prayer and the Bible ... 151
The Christian Life ... 169

1

ALLELUIA!

David Peacoc

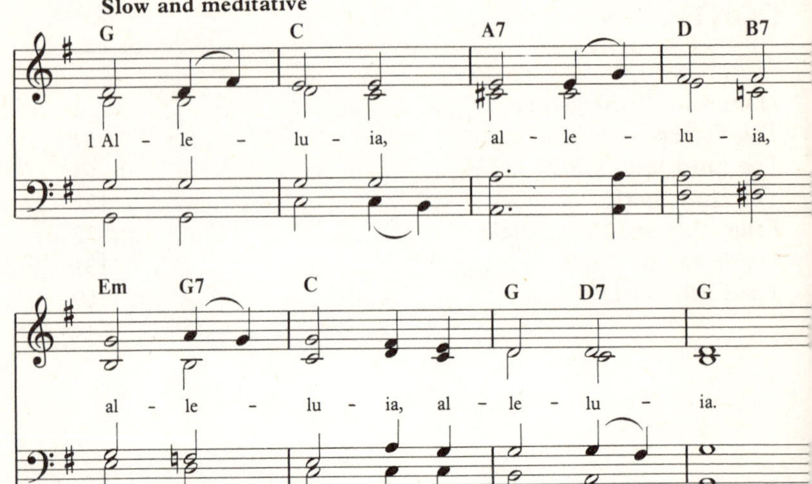
Slow and meditative
G C A7 D B7
1 Al - le - lu - ia, al - le - lu - ia,
Em G7 C G D7 G
al - le - lu - ia, al - le - lu - ia.

2 You are worthy,
you are worthy,
you are worthy
of all our praise.

3 Lord forgive us,
cleanse, remake us.
Lord, remember our
sin no more.

4 Lord we love you,
Lord we love you,
Lord we love you —
we love you Lord.

5 Alleluia, alleluia,
alleluia, alleluia!

Other verses can be added, for example: 'Lord we serve you; Lord we thank you', etc.

2

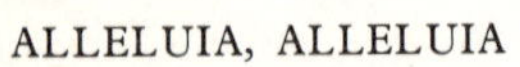

ALLELUIA, ALLELUIA

Don Fish
arr. Norman Warre

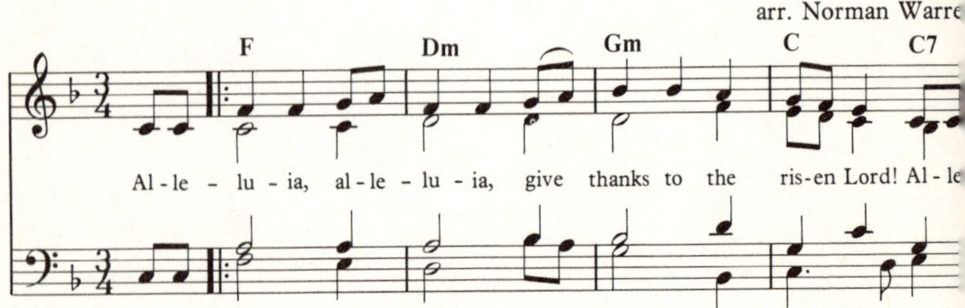
F Dm Gm C C7
Al - le - lu - ia, al - le - lu - ia, give thanks to the ris - en Lord! Al - le

F Dm Gm C7 F Fine F Dm Dm7
-lu - ia, al - le - lu - ia, give praise to his name. 1. Je - sus is Lord of
Gm C F Dm Gm C
all the earth. He is the King of cre - a - tion. Al-le -

Angela Reith

Chorus
(Alle-) al - le - lu - ia, al - le - lu - ia, thanks to the ris - en Lord.
Al - le - lu - ia, al - le - lu - ia, praise to his name.

2 Spread the good news through all the earth,
Jesus has died and has risen:
Alleluia, alleluia . . .

3 We have been crucified with Christ —
now we shall live for ever:
Alleluia, alleluia . . .

4 God has proclaimed the just reward —
life for all men, alleluia!
Alleluia, alleluia . . .

5 Come, let us praise the living God,
joyfully sing to our Saviour!
Alleluia, alleluia . . .

3

ALLELUIA! ALLELUIA!

Frank Hernande[z]
Arr. Betty Pulkinghan[m]

With abandon*
E A E A E A
1. Al - le - lu - ia!
1. Al - le -
E A E A E A
al - le - lu - ia! He is
- lu - ia! al - le - lu - ia!
B/D♯ E7/D A/C♯ Am/C
Lord, he is Lord. Al - le -
He is Lord, he is Lord. Al - le -

E/B F♯7/A♯ F♯m B7
-lu - ia, Je - sus is Lord!
-lu - ia, Je - sus is Lord!
1 2
F♯m B7 F♯m B7 F♯m7 B7
Al - le - Al - le - lu - ia,
Al - le - lu - ia,
F♯m7/B B7 E A E
Je - sus is Lord!
Je - sus is Lord!

2 Alleluia! Alleluia!
he is King, he is King.
Alleluia, Jesus is King!
(repeat)

Alleluia, Jesus is King!

4

ALLELUIA! FOR THE LORD OUR GOD

Dale Garratt

F F7 B♭ F Dm F C7 F C11
Al-le - lu - ia! for the Lord our God the al - migh - ty reigns; Al-le
F F7 B♭ F Dm F C7 F F7
- lu - ia! for the Lord our God the al - migh - ty reigns: Let us re-
B♭ C7 F C7 F Dm G G7 C C11
- joice and be glad and give the glo-ry un-to him: Al-le
F F7 B♭ F Dm F C7 F
- lu - ia! for the Lord our God the al - migh - ty reigns.

5

ALLELUIA! GOING TO SING ALL ABOUT IT

Unknown
Arr. David Peacock

E E7 A
Al - le - lu - ia! going to sing all a-bout it, Al - le - lu - ia! going to
A6 B7 E B7 E C♯m F♯
shout all a-bout it, Al - le - lu - ia! can't live with-out it: praise God!
B E E7 A
Now I'm liv-ing in a new cre-a - tion, now I'm drink-ing at the
A6 B7 E A6 E B7 E A E
well of sal- va - tion, now there is no con-dem-na - tion: praise God!

This can be followed by How great is our God (No. 58)

6

BREAK FORTH AND SING FOR JOY

Paul Armstrong
Arr. David Peacock

Psalm 100: v. 1–2

G D A7 D G D
Break forth and sing for joy. Break forth and
A7 D G D A7 D
sing for joy. Break forth and sing for joy and
1
Em Asus4 A
sing prai - ses.
2
G G♮dim D A7 Dsus4
sing prai - ses.
D Fine
D G D G D
Shout joy - ful - ly to the Lord

G Em D A D G
All the earth. Serve the Lord with
D Bm E7 Asus4 A7 G A7
glad - ness All the earth. Come be -
D Bm Em A7 D D7
fore him with joy - ful sing - ing.
D.C. al Fine
G Em D Bm Esus4 E7 Asus4 A7
Know that the Lord him - self is God.

7

CLAP YOUR HANDS (I)

Psalm 47

Words: Alan Warren
Music: Norman Warren

G
C
D7
G
C
D7

Chorus Unison
G
C
D7
G
C
D7
Clap your hands all you peo-ple Clap your hands all you peo-ple,

G
C
D7
G
C
D7
Wor-ship the Lord all your days, Trust in the Lord al - ways,

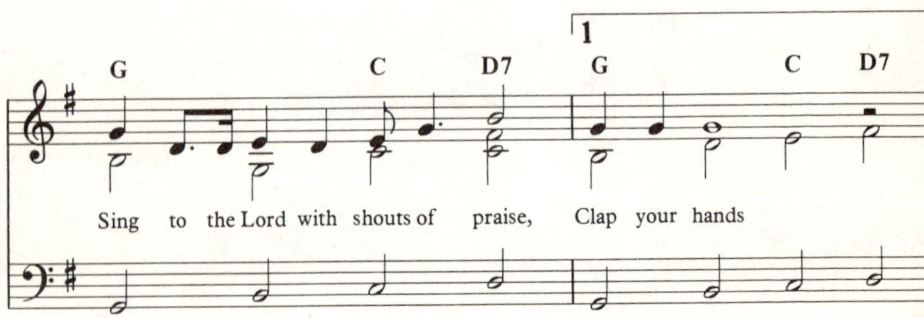
1
G
C
D7
G
C
D7
Sing to the Lord with shouts of praise, Clap your hands

Last time to Coda
2
Verse in Harmony
G C D7 G G7 C F G7
clap your hands,
clap your hands.
1. His peace will keep us,
2. His grace will save us,
C F G7 C Fm Bb
His life re - make us, His light will guide us,
His love re - fresh us, His joy will fill us,
Eb G#m C#7 F# Em7 A7
His hands will take us, His arms en - fold us, So,
His truth will teach us, His pow - er uplift us, So,
D D7
clap your hands,
clap your hands,
CODA
Clapping ad lib.
G C D7 G
clap your hands.

8

CLAP YOUR HANDS (II) (based on Psalm 47:1)

Jimmy Owens
Arr. David Peacock

1. C
2.
G7
C
Clap your hands all you peo - ple, Shout un - to God with a voice of tri - umph.
C
3.
C
4.
G7
C
Clap your hands all you peo - ple, Shout un - to God with a voice of praise! Ho -
C
G7
C
- san - na, Ho - san - na, Shout un - to God with a voice of tri - umph
C
C
G7
C
Praise Him, Praise Him, Shout un - to God with a voice of praise!

This may be sung as a round.

9

COME AND BLESS

Mimi Farra
Arr. Norman Warren

E A E A F♯m B7
1. Come and bless, come and praise, Come and praise the liv - ing God:
Chorus Al - le - lu, al - le - lu, al - le - lu - ia Je - sus Christ!
E A E to Coda A B7
Al - le - lu, al - le - lu, al - le - lu - ia Je - sus
Alternative Refrain only
E
Christ,
Otherwise
E
Christ.

Alternative Refrain

Norman Warren

A E F♯m C♯m
Glo - ry to the Son of God Glo - ry to our King
F♯m C♯m C Bsus4 B7
Glo - ry to our lov - ing Lord Glo - ry we will sing.
CODA
E A B7 E
Al - le - lu - ia, Je - sus Christ,
E A B7 E
al - le - lu - ia, Je - sus Christ,
p
E A Bsus4 B7 E
al - le - lu - ia, Je - sus Christ.
pp

2 Come and hear, come and know,
come and know the living God:
allelu, allelu, alleluia, Jesus Christ!
Allelu . . .*

3 Come and bless, come and praise,
come and praise the Word of God:
allelu, allelu, alleluia, Jesus Christ!
Allelu . . .

4 Angel choirs sing above,
'Glory to the Son of God!' —
joyful Christians sing below
'Alleluia, Jesus Christ!'
Allelu . . .

**Alternative Refrain*

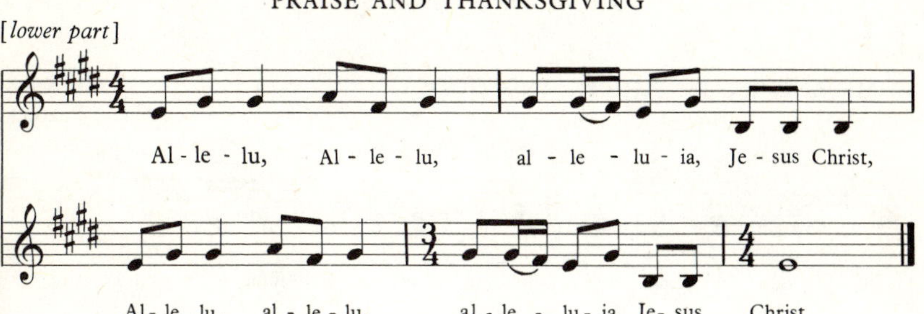
[lower part]
Al - le - lu, Al - le - lu, al - le - lu - ia, Je - sus Christ,
Al - le lu, al - le - lu, al - le - lu - ia, Je-, sus Christ

10

COME AND PRAISE HIM

A. Carter
Arr. Norman Warren

E F♯m B7 E B7 C♯m A A6 B E

1. Come and praise him, royal priesthood. Come and worship holy nation. Worship Jesus our Redeemer. He is precious, King of glory.

2. Come and praise him, God's own children. Come and worship chosen people. Worship Jesus our Redeemer. He is precious, King of glory.

11

COME AND PRAISE THE LIVING GOD

M. Kerry
Arr. David Peacock

Chorus
Bm
Bm7
Bm
F♯7
Come and praise the liv - ing God. Come and wor-ship,
Bm
Bm
Bm7
Bm
come and wor-ship. He has made you priest and king.
F♯7
Bm
Fine
Verses
Come and wor-ship the liv - ing God. 1. We
Verse 2
Bm
Bm7
Bm
2. By his voice he shakes the earth, His
Verse 1
come not to a moun-tain of fire and smoke,

Em
A7
D
judge – ments known through – out the world. But
Not to gloom and dark – ness or trum – pet sound. We

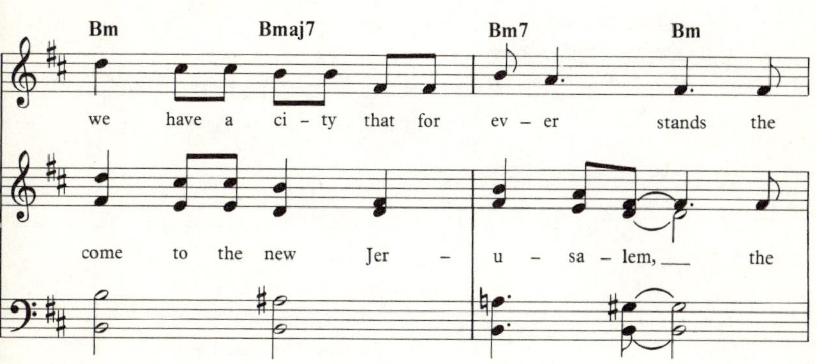
Bm
Bmaj7
Bm7
Bm
we have a ci – ty that for ev – er stands the
come to the new Jer – u – sa – lem, the

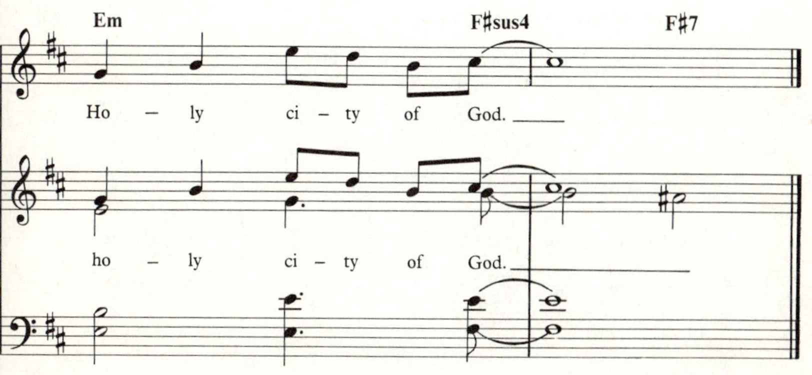
Em
F♯sus4
F♯7
Ho – ly ci – ty of God.
ho – ly ci – ty of God.

D.C. al Fine

12

COME BLESS THE LORD

Unknown
Arr. Norman Warren

C7
F
Ladies: Come bless the Lord
Men: Come bless the Lord
All you ser-vants of the

Gm
All you ser-vants of the Lord
C7
Gm
Who stand by
Lord
Who stand by night

C7
night
F
In the house of the Lord
In the house of the Lord
Lift up your

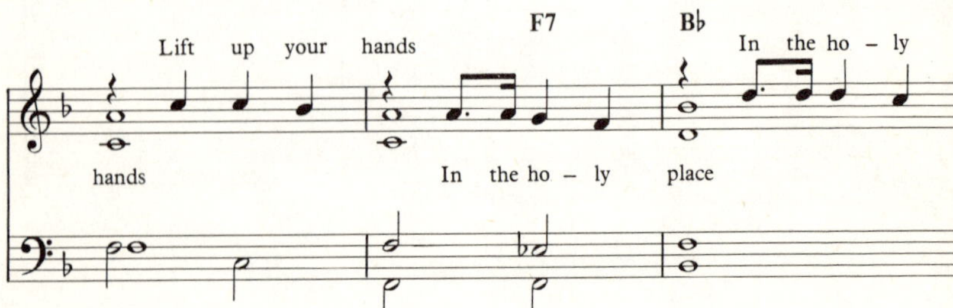
Lift up your hands
F7
B♭
In the ho - ly
hands
In the ho - ly place

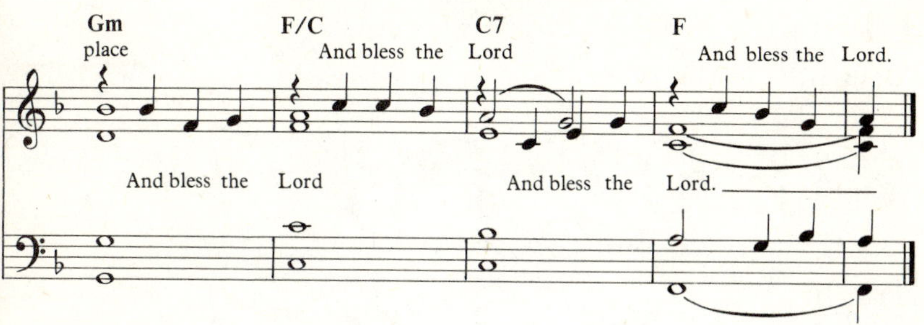
Gm F/C C7 F
place And bless the Lord And bless the Lord.
And bless the Lord And bless the Lord.

13

COME INTO HIS PRESENCE

Unknown
Arr. Norman Warren

C F C
Come in – to his pre – sence sing – ing al – le – lu – ia,

Am Em F E Am
al – le – lu – ia, al – le – lu – ia Come in – to his pre – sence sing – ing

Dm G7 C *Last time*
al – le – lu – ia.

Other verses. Come into his presence singing
2 Jesus is Lord . . .
3 Worthy the Lamb . . .
4 Glory to God . . .
5 Alleluia

14

COME SING PRAISES

Michael Perry
Arr. S. K. Coates

D G6
1. Come, sing prais - es to the Lord a - bove,
A7 D A+ D
Rock of our sal-va-tion, God of love; To his pre-sence with thanks
G6 Em A7 D D7
- giv - ing move For the Lord__ our God is King!
Chorus
G D A7
He's the King a-bove the moun-tains high, The sea is his,__ the
D A+ D B7 Em
land and sky__ Sub - ter - ran - ean depths that man de - fy__
to Coda

A7
D
Gm
D
Gm
D.C.
Are in the hol – low of his hand.

CODA (last Chorus)
A7
D
Gm
D
Are in the hol-low of his hand.
8ve

2 Here we worship him and bow the knee
for the shepherd of the flock is he;
mindful of his generosity,
sing the praise of God the king!
He's the king . . .

3 Hear a salutary story now,
you with stubborn hearts who will not bow;
mind his people that rebelled, and how
he showed them he was their king!
He's the king . . .

4 Forty years he kept their prize away,
made them wander till they walked his way;
exiled all of them until the day
they should honour him as king:
He's the king . . .

15

FATHER WE ADORE YOU

Terrye Coleho

G
C
D7
G
C
D7
G
C
D7
G
1. Fa-ther we a - dore you, lay our lives be - fore you: how we love you!

2 Jesus we adore you,
lay our lives before you:
how we love you!

3 Spirit we adore you,
lay our lives before you:
how we love you!

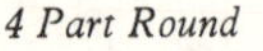

16

GLORY, PRAISE AND HONOUR

Unknown
Arr. Norman Warren

4 Part Round

1. B♭
F
2. B♭
F
Glo - ry, praise and hon - our we bring to him, the

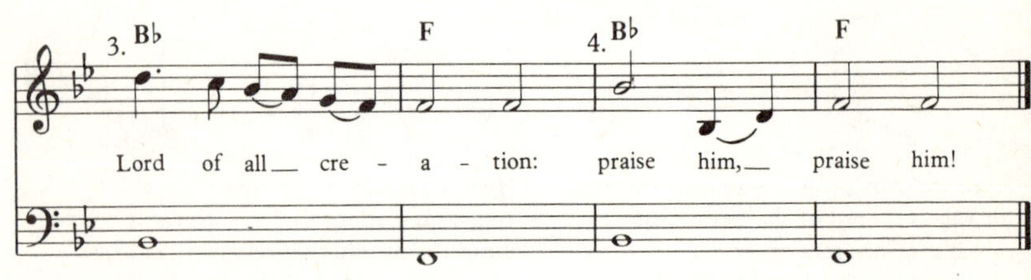
3. B♭
F
4. B♭
F
Lord of all cre - a - tion: praise him, praise him!

17

GLORY JESUS

Ron Griffith
Arr. David Peacock

Women:
D
F♯m
G
F♯m
Glo - - ry Je - sus
Men (tune):
1. Glo - ry to the king, Je - sus
2. Glo - ry to the king, Je - sus

PRAISE AND THANKSGIVING
D Em A
glo – ry, Je – sus
let our prais-es ring, Je – – sus
praise his ho-ly name, Je – – sus
D F♯m G D
glo – – ry, Je – sus,
bless him as we sing! Je – sus,
he is still the same! Je – sus,
Bm Em A7 D
Je – sus, Je – sus
Je – sus, Je – – sus.
Je – sus, Je – – sus.

18

HOLY, HOLY

Jimmy Owens

C Am Dm G7 Dm G7
1. Ho-ly, ho - ly, ho-ly, ho - ly, ho-ly, ho - ly Lord God al-
C C7 F Dm B7 Em Am
-migh - ty! And we lift our hearts be-fore you as a to-ken of our love: ho - ly,
Dm G7 1–5 C 6 C
ho - ly, ho - ly, ho - ly.
Ped.

2 Gracious Father, gracious Father,
we're so glad to be your children, gracious Father;
and we lift our heads before you
as a token of our love,
gracious Father, gracious Father.

3 Precious Jesus, precious Jesus,
we're so glad that you've redeemed us, precious Jesus;
and we lift our hands before you
as a token of our love,
precious Jesus, precious Jesus.

4 Holy Spirit, Holy Spirit,
come and fill our hearts anew, Holy Spirit! —
and we lift our voice before you
as a token of our love,
holy Spirit, holy Spirit.

5 Hallelujah, hallelujah,
hallelujah, hallelujah! —
and we lift our hearts before you
as a token of our love:
hallelujah, hallelujah!

19

HOLY, HOLY, HOLY IS THE LORD

Unknown
Arr. Norman Warren

A F♯m C♯m D
1. Ho - ly, ho - ly, ho - ly is the Lord; ho - ly is the
E 1 2 D Bm E C♯m F♯m
Lord God al - migh - ty! -ty, who was, and is, and is to
E A F♯m Bm E7 A
come: ho - ly, ho - ly, ho - ly is the Lord!

2 Jesus, Jesus, Jesus is the Lord;
Jesus is the Lord God almighty . . .

3 Worthy, worthy, worthy is the Lord;
worthy is the Lord God almighty . . !

4 Glory, glory, glory to the Lord;
glory to the Lord God almighty . . !

20

I WILL ENTER HIS GATES

Unknown
Arr. David Peacock

E A E B7 E
I will en-ter his gates with thanks giv-ing in my heart, I will en-ter his
A F♯7 B E B B11 E A
courts with praise; I will say this is the day that the
E B7 C♯m F♯m B7 E A E
Lord has made, I will re-joice for he has made me glad.
E A F♯7 E B7 C♯m Fm
He has made me glad, he has made me glad I will re-joice for
1 2
B7 E B7 E B7 B7 E A E
he has made me glad. he has made me glad.

21

I WILL SING, I WILL SING

Max Dyer

E
A
E
1. I will sing, I will sing a song un - to the Lord, I will

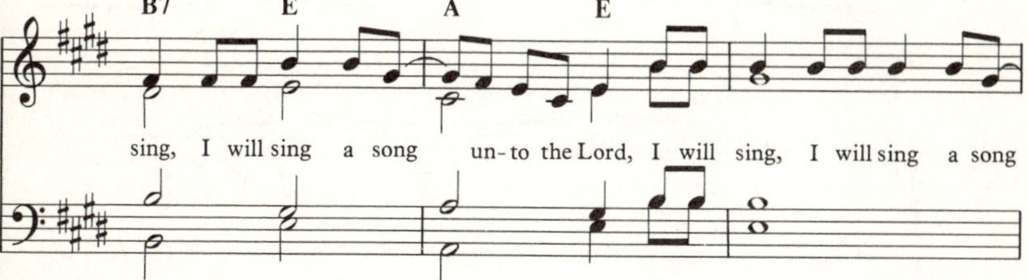
B7
E
A
E
sing, I will sing a song un - to the Lord, I will sing, I will sing a song

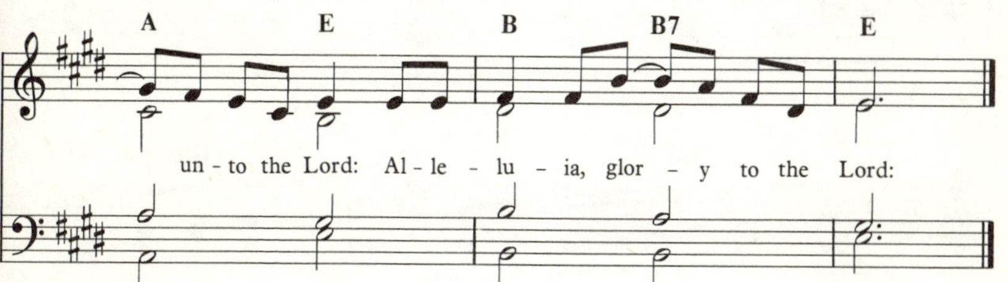
A
E
B
B7
E
un - to the Lord: Al - le - lu - ia, glor - y to the Lord:

Chorus: Allelu, alleluia, glory to the Lord, *(three times)*
Alleluia, glory to the Lord.

2 We will come, we will come as one before the Lord, . .
alleluia, glory to the Lord!
Allelu, alleluia . . .

3 If the Son, if the Son shall make you free, . .
you shall be free indeed:
Allelu, alleluia . . .

4 They that sow in tears shall reap in joy, . .
alleluia, glory to the Lord!
Allelu, alleluia . . .

This song is suitable for unaccompanied singing.

22

IN THE PRESENCE OF YOUR PEOPLE

Psalm 22:3, 25

Brent Chambers

Joyfully, well accented

A7 Dm A7 Dm A7 Dm

1. In the pres-ence of your peo - ple I will praise your name,
2. Lai - lai - lai - lai - lai - lai - lai . . . . .

D Gm C F B♭ Gm A7

for a - lone you are ho - ly, en - throned on the prais - es of Is - ra - el.

Dm A7 Dm A7 Dm

Let us cel - e - brate your good - ness and your stead - fast - love,

D Gm C F B♭ Gm A7 Dm

May your name be ex - alt - ed here on earth and in heav'n a - bove.

This song may be started at a leisurely speed and sung several times with gradual acceleration of tempo. Out of doors or in a large area there is exciting potential for a circle dance.

23

THE JOY OF THE LORD IS MY STRENGTH

Alliene Vale
Arr. Norman Warren

D
A7
1. The joy of the Lord is my strength, the

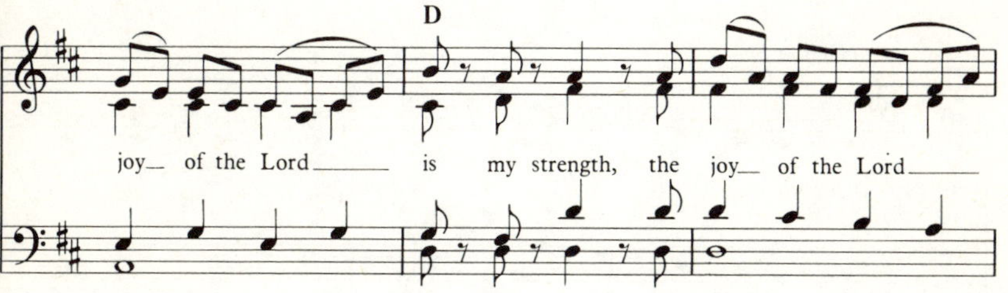
D
joy of the Lord is my strength, the joy of the Lord

G
D
A7
D
is my strength, the joy of the Lord is my strength!

2 If you want joy, you must sing for it,
if you want joy, you must sing for it,
if you want joy, you must sing for it:
the joy of the Lord is my strength!

3 If you want joy, you must shout for it,
if you want joy, you must shout for it,
if you want joy, you must shout for it:
the joy of the Lord is my strength!

4 If you want joy, you must jump for it,
if you want joy, you must jump for it,
if you want joy, you must jump for it:
the joy of the Lord is my strength!

24

JUBILATE DEO — *A Round*

Unknown

1.
2.
3.
Ju - bi - la - te De - o, ju - bi - la - te De - o, Al - le - lu - ia.

25

JUBILATE EVERYBODY

Words and Music: Michael Perry
Arr. Stephen Coates and Norman Warren

Introduction
Verse
F
1. Ju - bi - la - te

F
Dm7
B♭
C7
ev - ery - bo - dy, serve the Lord with glad - ness;

F
F
F
Dm7
O be joy - ful ev - ery - bo - dy come be - fore him

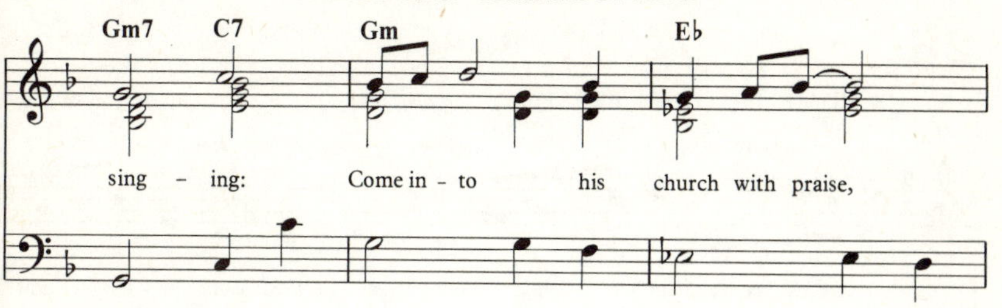
Gm7
C7
Gm
E♭
sing - ing: Come in - to his church with praise,

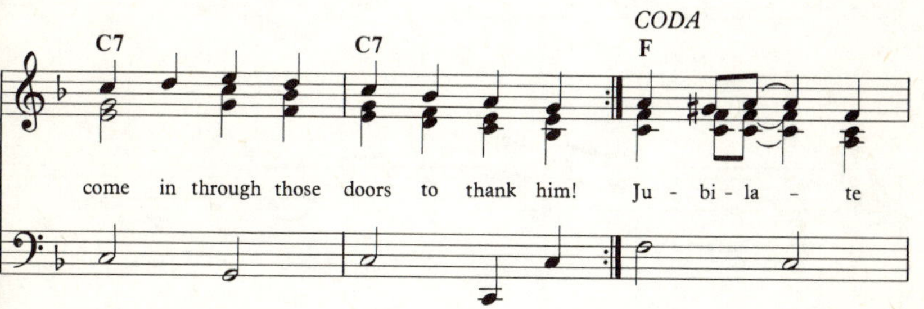
CODA
C7
C7
F
come in through those doors to thank him! Ju - bi - la - te

F
F
Dm7
Gm7
C7
F
ev - ery-bo - dy. Ju - bi - la - te De - o!

2 Know that he, the God who made us,
he it is who owns us;
we, the people of his care,
the sheep upon his hillside:
Come into his church with praise,
come in through those doors to thank him!

3 For the Lord our God is good —
his love is everlasting;
and his faithfulness endures
to every generation:
Come into his church with praise
come in through those doors to thank him!

Jubilate everybody.
Jubilate De-o!

26

LET US COME INTO HIS PRESENCE (Psalm 95)

Norman Warren

G
Em
Am
1. Let us come in - to his pre - sence, the Lord of hea-ven and
Ped.
Ped.
Ped.
D
Bm
Em
earth! — let us sing to him with tri - umph, our
Ped.
Ped.
Fine
Chorus
Am
D7
G
E♭
rock, our sa - viour, friend: All glo - ry, - praise and
D
Cm
Am
D7
hon - our, be his for ev - er - more — let us

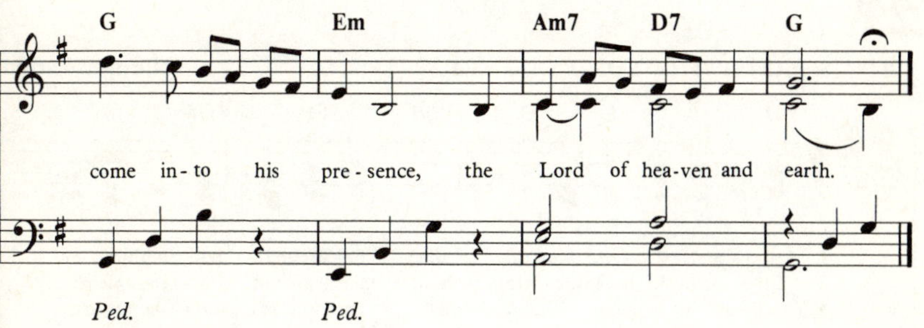
G
Em
Am7
D7
G
come in-to his pre-sence, the Lord of hea-ven and earth.
Ped.
Ped.

2 Let us come before him with thanksgiving,
and sing to him with psalms:
he is king above all creation,
the Lord is a mighty God:
All glory . . .

3 In his hand the depths of the earth,
the mountain peaks are his;
the sea is his and he made it —
he formed the dry land:
All glory . . .

4 Let us kneel before our maker
for he himself is our God! —
we are the people of his pasture,
the sheep of his hand:
All glory . . .

5 All glory to the Father,
all glory to the Son,
all glory to the Holy Spirit,
for evermore! Amen:
All glory . . .

27

LET US PRAISE THE LORD OUR GOD

Norman Warren

D G D Bm F♯m G6 A7
1. Let us praise the Lord our God, come be-fore him, shout his prais-es:
2. In his hands he holds the earth, moun - tains high and o - ceans deep;
3. This great God is our God — let us kneel to him who made us;
D G D Bm F♯m G6 A
Chorus
C
let us sing with thankful hearts, come be - fore him full of joy!
ev - ery val - ley ev - ery hill, all cre - a - tion they are his:
shep-herd of the flock is he, he will guide us with his hand:
Ev - ery throne must
F C E♭ A♭ E♭ D
bow to him, he is Lord of ev - ery - thing: praise our ma - ker,
v. 1, 2
v. 3
G F♯m G6 A7 D G F♯ B
praise our sa-viour, praise the Lord our king!
king!

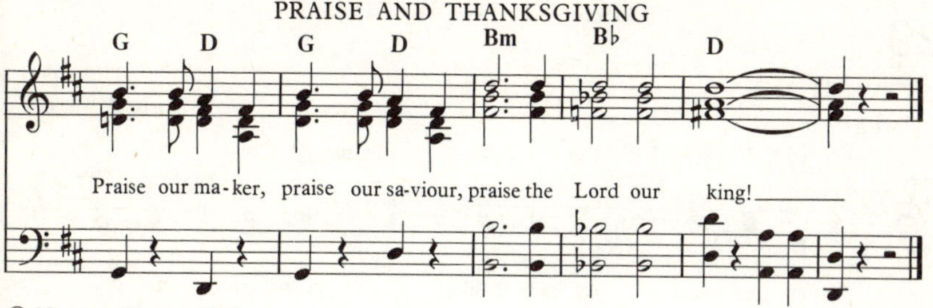
PRAISE AND THANKSGIVING
G D G D Bm B♭ D
Praise our ma-ker, praise our sa-viour, praise the Lord our king!

28

MARY SANG A SONG

Words and Music: Michael Perry

Dm Dm7 Dm F Dm B♭ A

1. Ma-ry sang a song, a song of love, mag-ni-fied the migh-ty Lord a-bove;

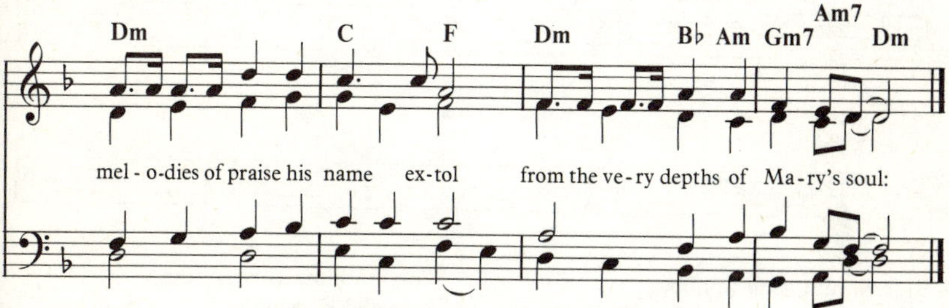

Dm C F Dm B♭ Am Gm7 Am7 Dm

mel-o-dies of praise his name ex-tol from the ve-ry depths of Ma-ry's soul:

2 'God the Lord has done great things for me,
looked upon my life's humility;
happy, they shall call me from this day —
merciful is he whom we obey.

3 'To the humble soul our God is kind,
to the proud he brings unease of mind:
who uplifts the poor, pulls down the strong? —
God alone has power to right the wrong.

4 'He who has been Israel's strength and stay
fills the hungry, sends the rich away;
he has shown his promise firm and sure
faithful to his people evermore.'

5 This was Mary's song as we recall,
mother to the saviour of us all:
magnify his name and sing his praise
worship and adore him all your days!

29

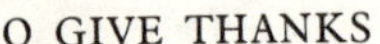

O GIVE THANKS

Unknown
Arr. Norman Warren

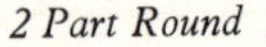

2 Part Round

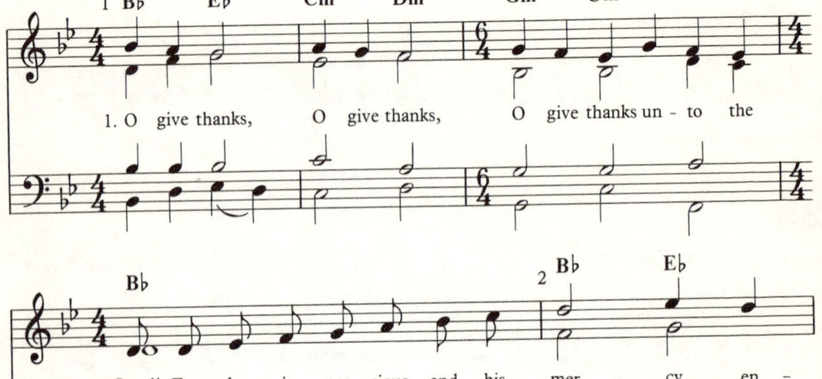
1. O give thanks, O give thanks, O give thanks un - to the

Lord! For he is gra - cious and his mer - cy en -

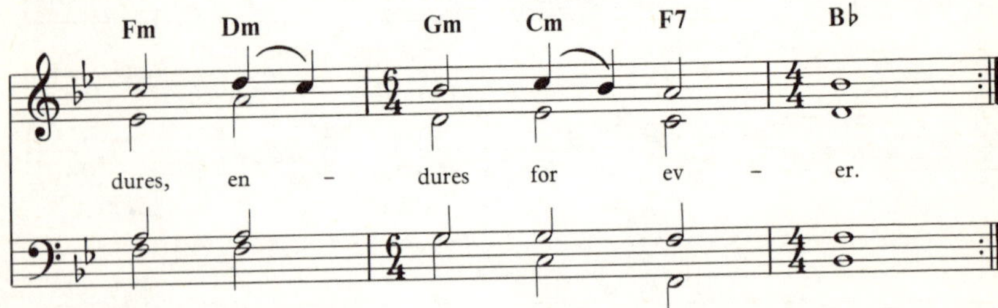
dures, en - dures for ev - er.

2 Sing to him, sing to him,
sing a new song to the Lord!
for he is gracious and his mercy endures,
endures for ever.

3 Worship him, worship him,
come and worship our great God!
for he is gracious and his mercy endures,
endures for ever.

30

O HOW GOOD IS THE LORD

Unknown
Arr. Norman Warren

Chorus
O how good is the Lord, O how good is the Lord,

C7
F
C
F6
O how good is the Lord, I nev-er will for-get what he has

C
G7
C
Fine
Verse
C
Dm
done for me! 1. He gives me sal-va-tion, how good is the Lord, he

G7
C
C
C7
gives me sal-va-tion, how good is the Lord, he gives me sal-va-tion, how

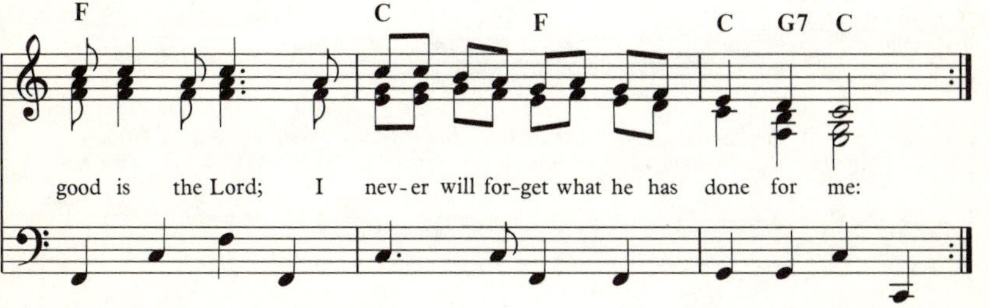
F
C
F
C
G7
C
good is the Lord; I nev-er will for-get what he has done for me:

2 He gives me his blessings . . .
O how good . . !

3 He gives me his Spirit . . .
O how good . . !

4 He gives me his healing . . .
O how good . . !

5 He gives me his glory . . .
O how good . . !

O PRAISE THE LORD (Psalm 149)

Norman Warren

Chorus
D Em A7 D
O praise the Lord, O praise the Lord,
G Em A7
sing to the Lord a new song,
sing out his praises
Em A7 D
all peo - ple of God.
Fine
D7
Verse
G
1. Let us praise him
2. Vic - to - ry be -
C G Am Em
in the dance, let us praise him on the strings,
- longs to him, jus - tice mer - cy truth are his,
F G Em7 A7
let us all be joy - ful in our king:
for the Lord takes plea - sure in his peo - ple:

32

PRAISE GOD FROM WHOM ALL BLESSINGS FLOW

Music: Thomas Tallis

(Tallis Canon)

1.
2.

Praise God from whom all bless-ings flow, in heaven a - bove and earth be - low;

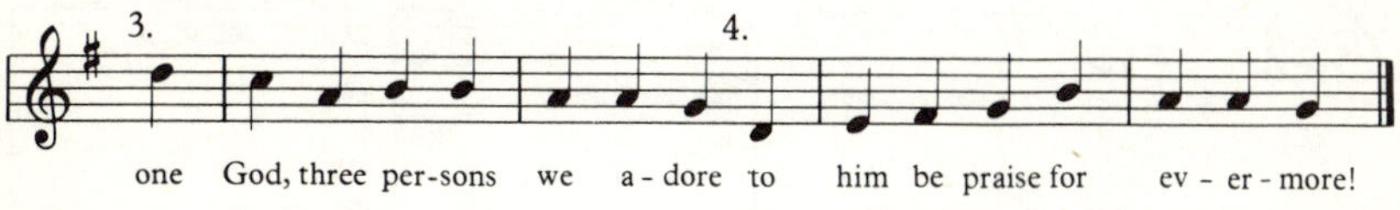
3.
4.
one God, three per-sons we a - dore to him be praise for ev - er - more!

33

PRAISE GOD FROM WHOM ALL BLESSINGS FLOW

Music: Jimmy Owens
Arr. David Peacock

E G♯m A E E7 A B7

Praise God from whom all bless - ings flow, in heaven a -

G♯m C♯m F♯m B7 E G♯m

- bove and earth be - low; one God, three per - sons,

A E A E E7 B7 E

we a - dore — to him be praise for ever - - more!

34

PRAISE THE LORD IN HIS HOLINESS (Psalm 150) — Norman Warren

Strong rhythm, not too fast
F Gm Am Gm F Gm Am Gm
F Gm Am Gm F Gm
1. Praise the Lord in his ho-li-ness, Praise him for his migh-ty
2. Let the trum-pet sing his glo - ry, Let the strings re-sound in
3. Praise him with the sound of mu - sic, Let the whole world sing with
Am Dm
v. 1, 2
Gm Am B♭ C A
power. Praise him in the high-est hea - ven Praise him peo - ple
praise. Drum and cym-bal crash in har-mo-ny.
joy.
(Choir)
Praise him peo-ple
org.

v. 1, 2
Gm C7
here on earth.
Eve - ry liv - ing crea - ture
here on earth.
organ
F Fm D
praise him. Praise the migh - ty Lord.
G Am B♭ Am G Am
Trumpet
Bm Am G Am Bm Am
4. Glo - ry to the heaven-ly Fa - ther

G Am Bm Em Am Bm

glo – ry to the roy - al Son, Glo – ry to the Ho - ly

Am D D7 G

Spi – rit; Praise him Praise our God.

Praise him

(Choir)

org.

35

PRAISE THE LORD (Psalm 146)

Spanish Folk Tune
Adapted and arranged by Norman Warren

G C G C G

1. Praise the

Am7 D7 G

Lord, Praise the Lord my soul!

Am7
D7
I'll praise the Lord ___ as long as I
G
G7
Chorus
C
Cmin6
live: _ _ _ _ _ And I will sing a song, sing a song,
Bmin
E
Am7
sing a song to him, a song of praise ___
D
G
Last time
G
___ to my God all my life.

Use Tambourines, Maracas, Castanets with rhythms or or

2 Happy the man with the Lord to help him;
happy the man who depends on the Lord:
And I will sing . . .

3 The Lord is king, he is king for evermore;
the Lord is king, he will reign for all time:
And I will sing . . .

36

PRAISE YOU FATHER

Jim Stipech
Arr. David Peacock

Gently
Descant:
E
B7
Praise you Fa - ther!
Praise you Fa - ther!
bless you
bless you Je - sus!
E E7 A F♯m
Je - sus!
Ho - ly Spir - it,
Ho - ly Spir - it, thank you for
E B7 E Amaj7 E
thank you, thank you, Lord.
being here, being here! Lord!

PREPARE THE WAY OF THE LORD

Mary Smail

Ch.
C Em F C Dm G
1. Pre - pare the way of the Lord Make his paths straight

Dm G F G7 C Em F C
o - pen the gates that he may en - ter free - ly in - to our lives. Ho

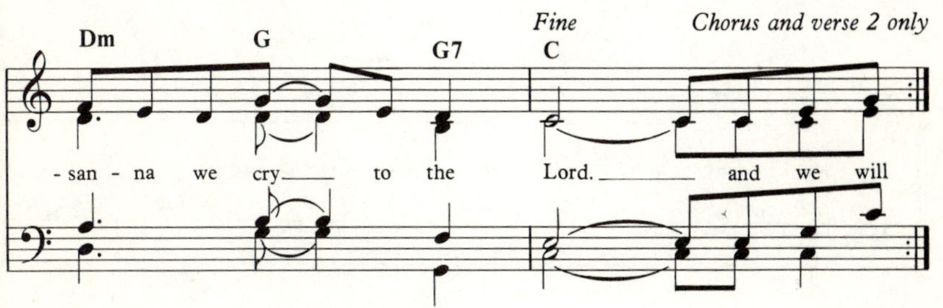
Fine
Chorus and verse 2 only
Dm G G7 C
- san - na we cry to the Lord. and we will

And we will fill the earth
with the sound of his praise —
Jesus is Lord! let him be adored!
Yes, we will have this man to reign over us,
hosanna! we follow the Lord.

2 And he will come to us as he came before,
clothed in his glory, to stand in our place;
and we behold him, now our priest, Lord and king:
Hosanna! we sing to the Lord.
And we will . . .

3 Prepare the way of the Lord!
make his paths straight;
open the gates that he may enter freely
into our lives:
Hosanna! we cry to the Lord.
And we will . . .

38

REJOICE IN THE LORD ALWAYS

Evelyn Tarner
Arr. Norman Warren

G D7 1 G

*Re - joice in the Lord al - ways and a - gain I say re - joice Re -

2 G D7

joice, *Re - joice, Re - joice and a - gain I say re -

G D7 G

- joice Re - joice, Re - joice and a - gain I say re - joice.

*This may be sung as a 2 part round.

39

SING A NEW SONG

Words: Timothy Dudley-Smith
Music: David G. Wilson

G F G F G Dm
1. Sing a new song to the Lord, he to whom won-ders be

PRAISE AND THANKSGIVING
(v. 1)
(v. 3 & 4)
(v. 3)
G F Em A
long; re - joice in his tri - umph and
with trumpet
and horn
Em F D7 G Dm7
tell of his power O sing to the
1st time etc.
Last verse
Am D7 G Am7 G Am7 G
Lord a new song!

2 Now to the ends of the earth
see his salvation is shown;
and still he remembers his mercy and truth,
unchanging in love to his own.

3 Sing a new song and rejoice,
publish his praises abroad;
let voices in chorus, with trumpet and horn,
resound for the joy of the Lord!

4 Join with the hills and the sea,
thunders of praise to prolong;
in judgement and justice he comes to the earth —
O sing to the Lord a new song!

40

SING AND REJOICE
Unknown
Round
1. Sing and re - joice, sing and re - joice,—
2. Heaven's prais - es ring, heaven's prais - es ring—
3. Your voi - ces raise, your voi - ces raise—
Je - sus is ri - sen: come, lift up your voice!
Je - sus is ri - sen: to him we will sing.
Je - sus has saved us: come give him due praise.
© J. Curwen & Sons Ltd, London
41
SING HIS PRAISES
M. Cox
G Em C D G C G A D
Sing his prais - es! hea - ven rais - es songs of him who died for me;
Bm Em Am D G C G D G
his the glo - ry, mine the sto - ry of the love which sets me free;
D C D7 G C G Em A7 D
love which nev - er will de-ceive me, love which nev - er lets me go:

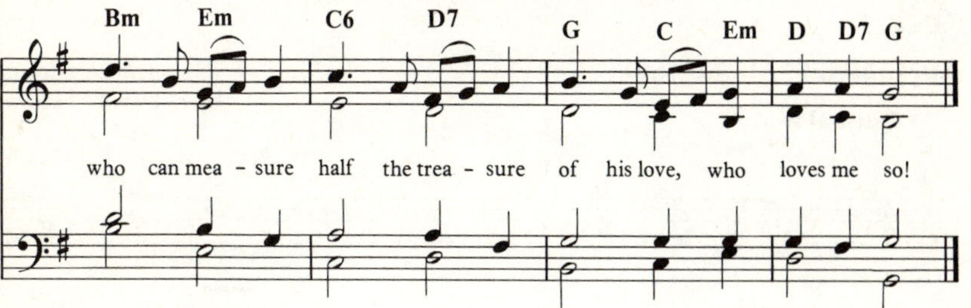
Bm Em C6 D7 G C Em D D7 G
who can mea - sure half the trea - sure of his love, who loves me so!

42

SING WE A SONG

Fred Kaan
Arr. Norman Warren

G B C D G Em Am D
1. Sing we a song of high re - volt — make great the Lord his — name ex - alt:

G B Em C G Em D7 G
sing we the song that Ma - ry sang, Of God at war with hu - man wrong.

2 Sing we of him who deeply cares,
and still with us our burden bears;
he who with strength the proud disowns,
brings down the mighty from their thrones:

3 By him the poor are lifted up —
he satisfies with bread and cup
the hungry men of many lands;
the rich must go with empty hands.

4 He calls us to revolt and fight
with him for what is just and right;
to sing and live Magnificat
in crowded street and council flat.

43

SOMETIMES 'ALLELUIA!'

Chuck Girard
Arr. David Peacock

Quite slow
Chorus
C
F
G
Some-times 'Al - le - lu - ia!' some-times 'Praise the
C
F
A7
Dm
Lord!' some - times gent - ly sing - ing
G7
C
Fine
Verses
C
G7
our hearts in one ac - cord.
1. O let us lift our
F
C
F
G7
voi - ces, look to - ward the sky and start to

F C
F
G7
sing; ——
O let us now re - turn his

Da Capo to Chorus
Em A
Dm
C G7
love ——
just let our voi - ces ring!

2 O let us feel his presence,
let the sound of praises fill the air;
O let us sing the song of Jesus' love,
to people everywhere!
Sometimes 'Alleluia!' . .

3 O let our joy be unconfined —
let us sing with freedom unrestrained;
let's take this feeling that we feel now,
outside these walls and let it ring!
Sometimes 'Alleluia!' . .

4 O let the Spirit overflow,
as we are filled from head to toe:
we love you Father, Son and Spirit,
and we want the world to know!
Sometimes 'Alleluia!' . .

44

STAND UP, CLAP HANDS

Words: Roger Dyer
Music: Allan Forrest

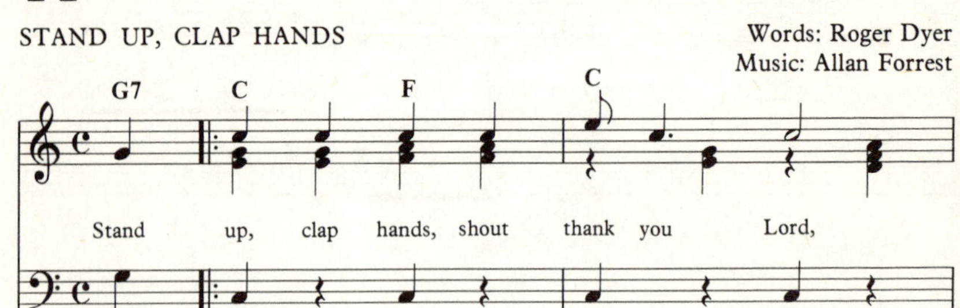
G7 C F C
Stand up, clap hands, shout thank you Lord,

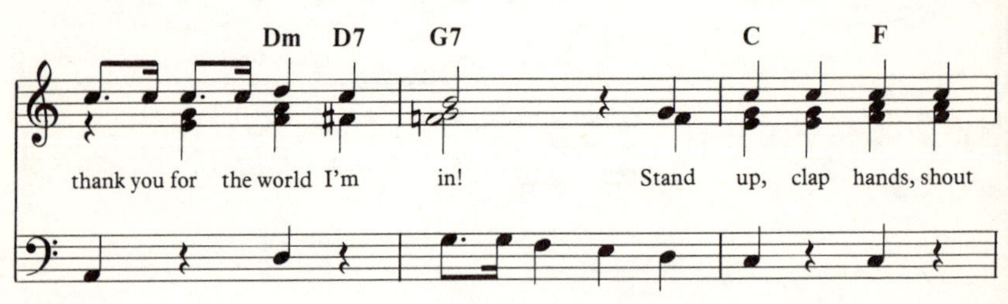
Dm D7 G7 C F
thank you for the world I'm in! Stand up, clap hands, shout

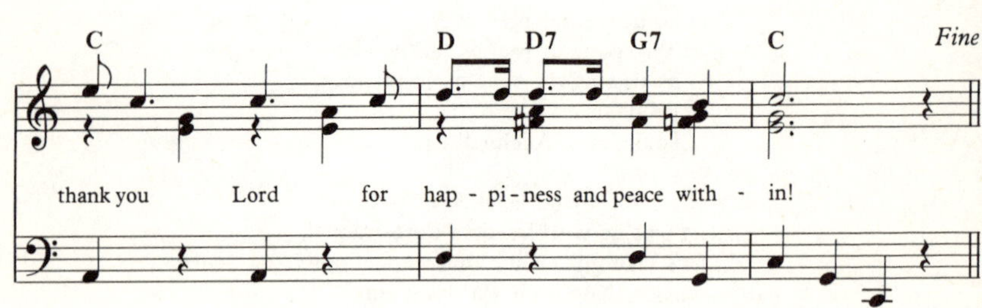
C D D7 G7 C Fine
thank you Lord for hap - pi - ness and peace with - in!

Verse
C F C F
1. I look a - round and the sun's in the sky

C F C F D7 G
I look a - round_ and then I think Oh my! the world is such a
D7 G7 D D7 G7
won - der-ful place,_ and all be - cause of the good Lord's grace. Stand

2 I look around and the creatures I see,
I look around and it amazes me
that every fox and bird and hare
must fit in a special place somewhere.
Stand up, clap hands . . .

3 I look around at all the joy I've had,
I look around and then it makes me glad
that I can offer thanks and praise,
to him who guides me through my days.
Stand up, clap hands . . .

45

THEN SHALL THE YOUNG GIRLS REJOICE

Merla Watson
Arr. David Peacock

Lively

Dm A7 Dm A7

1. Then shall the young girls re - joice___ in the dance, the
2. Li li li li . . . . .

Gm 1 A

young___ men and old___ men to - geth - er:

2 A Dm Gm

li li li: Then I shall turn their mourn-ing in - to

Dm A Dm A Gm

joy; then I will com - fort

Dm D Gm7 C
them and make them re - joice,

Fmaj7 B♭ Gm6 A
re - joice from their

Dm A D Gm7 C
sor - row; and make them re - joice,

*Repeat twice, faster each time
Fmaj7 B♭ Gm6 A Dm
re - joice in the Lord.

46

THEREFORE THE REDEEMED

Ruth Lake

B♭
There-fore the re-deemed of the Lord shall re – turn ___ and come with
E♭ B♭ E♭ B♭
sing-ing ___ un-to Zi-on, ___ and e-ver-last-ing ___ joy shall be up-on their
1 B♭ E♭ B♭ 2 B♭ E♭ B♭
head. ___ There-fore the re- head. ___ They shall ob –
E♭ B♭ F B♭
– tain ___ glad – ness and joy ___ and
C F
sor – row and mourn-ing shall flee a – way: ___ There-fore the re-

B♭
E♭
-deemed of the Lord shall re-turn ___ and come with sing-ing ___ un-to
Cm
B♮
E♭
F
B♭
Zi-on, ___ and ev-er-last-ing joy shall be up-on their head.

47

THEREFORE WE LIFT OUR HEARTS

Words: Mary Smail & Colin Greene
Music: David Smail
Arr. Norman Warren

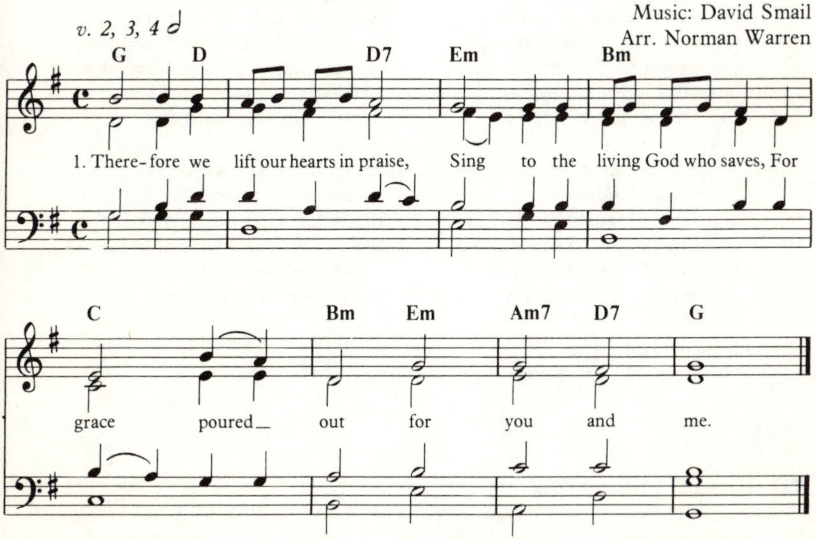

v. 2, 3, 4 𝅗𝅥

G D D7 Em Bm

1. There-fore we lift our hearts in praise, Sing to the living God who saves, For

C Bm Em Am7 D7 G

grace poured_ out for you and me.

2 There for everyone to see,
there on the hill at Calvary
Jesus died for you and me.

3 There for sad and broken men
he rose up from the grave again,
and reigns on high for you and me.

4 There for such great pain and cost
the Spirit came at Pentecost
and comes in power for you and me.

5 Therefore we lift our hearts in praise,
sing to the living God who saves,
for grace poured out for you and me.

48

THEY SAY HE'S WONDERFUL

Words: Hugh Pollock
Trad. arr. Norman Warren

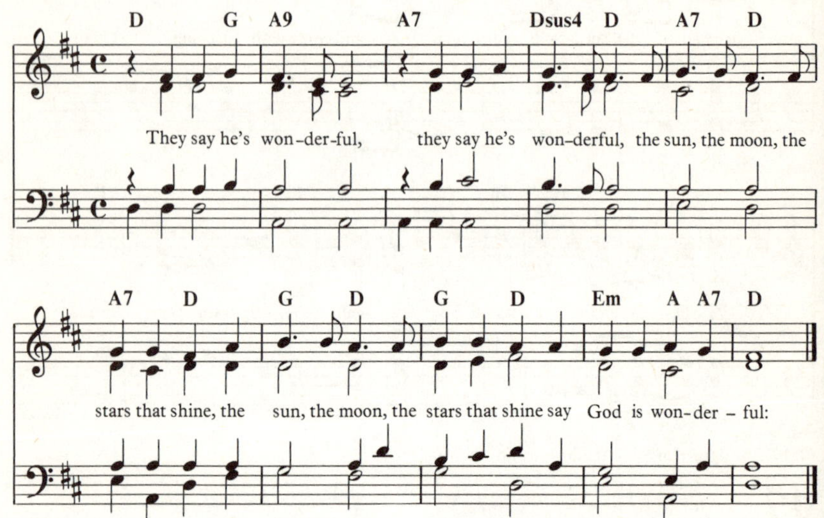
D G A9 A7 Dsus4 D A7 D
They say he's won-der-ful, they say he's won-derful, the sun, the moon, the
A7 D G D G D Em A A7 D
stars that shine, the sun, the moon, the stars that shine say God is won-der - ful:

1 He makes the rain to fall,
he sees the wheat grow tall,
the harvest of the land and sea,
the harvest of the land and sea,
in love he gives it all.
They say he's wonderful . . .

2 When I see babies small,
and I hear children call,
and think of family life and fun,
and think of family life and fun,
I know he's behind it all.
They say he's wonderful . . .

3 The love men have for him —
such love death cannot dim,
of small and great of rich and poor,
of small and great of rich and poor —
love like this comes from him.
They say he's wonderful . . .

4 And I know he's wonderful,
I know he's wonderful;
the Son of God who died for me
the Son of God who died for me —
I know he's wonderful.
They say he's wonderful . . .

49

TO GOD BE THE GLORY

Andrae Crouch

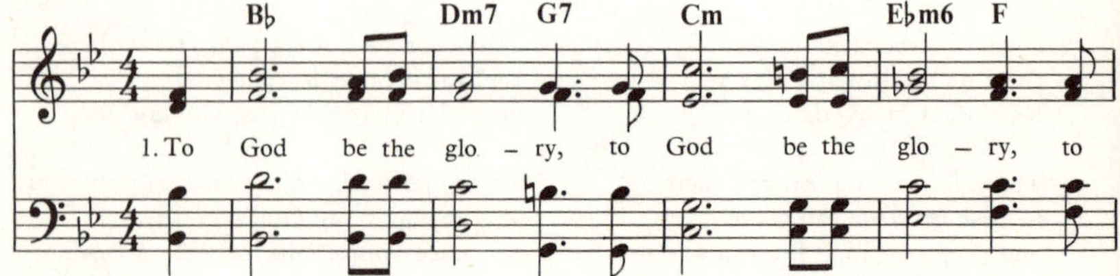
B♭ Dm7 G7 Cm E♭m6 F
1. To God be the glo - ry, to God be the glo - ry, to

PRAISE AND THANKSGIVING
D7 Gmsus Gm C7 F7
God be the glo - ry for the things he has done! With his
B♭ Dm7 G7 Cm E♭m6 F
blood he has saved me, with his power he has raised me: to
D7 Gmsus C7 E♭m6/G♭ B♭/F E♭/F B♭ Fine B♭ Optional ending
God be the glo – ry for the things he has done! done! Just let me
D7/A Cm/A D7 Gm
live my life, let it be pleas - ing Lord, to you; and if I
E♭ Gm C7 F7 D.S.
gain an - y praise, Let it go to Cal – va – ry! With his

Capo 2 (G)

50

WE CRY, HOSANNA, LORD

Mimi Farra

Brightly
Refrain
A(G)
F♯m(Em)
We cry, ho - san - na, Lord; yes, ho - san - na, Lord; yes, ho -
Dmaj7(Cmaj7)
E(D)
A(G)
- san - na, Lord, to __ you! We cry, ho - san - na, Lord, yes, ho -
F♯m(Em)
D(C)
E(D)
A(G)
Fine
- san - na, Lord, yes, ho - san - na, Lord, __ to you!
A(G)
D(C)
A(G)
D(C)
1. Be - hold, our sav - iour comes! Be - hold the Son of our
3. He comes to set us free,
2. Child - ren wave their palms as the King of all __ Kings rides __
(3.) he gives __ us lib - er -

E(D)
Bm(Am)
E(D7)
(1.) God: he of – fers him – self and he
(2.) by: should we for – get to praise our
(3.) -ty; his vict – ory o – ver death is the
A(G)
F♯m(Em)
D(C)
E(D)
D.C.
(1.) comes a – mong us, a low – ly ser – vant to all.
(2.) God, the ve – ry stones would sing.
(3.) eter – nal sign of God's love for us.
descant for refrain
(This descant is most effective when sung by higher men's voices.)
Ho - san - na! Ho - san - na! Ho - san-na to
you. Ho - san - na! Ho - san - na! Ho - sanna to you.

51

WE MAGNIFY YOUR NAME, LORD

Pam Hansford
Arr. Norman Warren

F
Gm Dm7 Gm Dm
C7 F
We mag-ni-fy your name, Lord; we worship and a – dore you
Bb C C7 F Bb F C7
for who you are, for what you've done a-mong your peo – ple
F C7 F Gm C7 F
here: we o-pen up our lives to you, lay down our minds and wills;
A A7 Dm A Dm Bb F C7 F
we want you Lord to have your way, for we de-light in you.

52

WHEREVER I AM

Unknown
Arr. David Peacock

Quite Fast
G Am D7 G
Where-e-ver I am I'll praise him, when e-ver I can I'll
C G C G A7 F
praise him; For his love ___ sur-rounds me like a sea: ___
D7 E7 Am D7 G A9 B7
___ I'll praise the name of Je-sus, lift up the name of
Em F♯dim E7 Am G D7 G C G
Je-sus, For the name of Je-sus lift-ed me. ___

53

YOUR LOVING KINDNESS

Hugh Mitchell
Arr. David Peacock

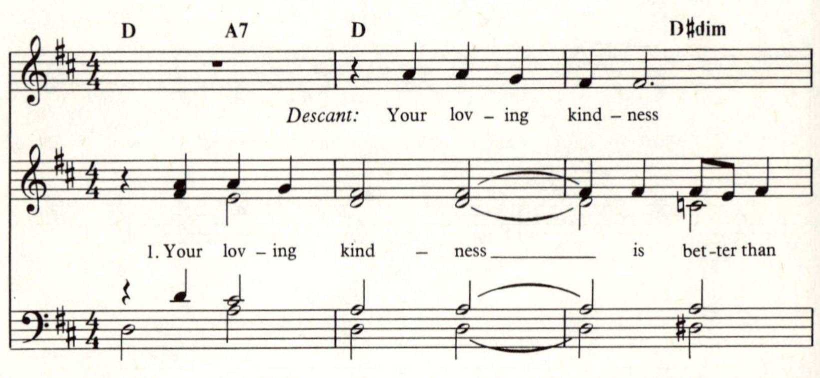
D
A7
D
D♯dim
Descant: Your lov – ing kind – ness
1. Your lov – ing kind – ness ___ is bet-ter than

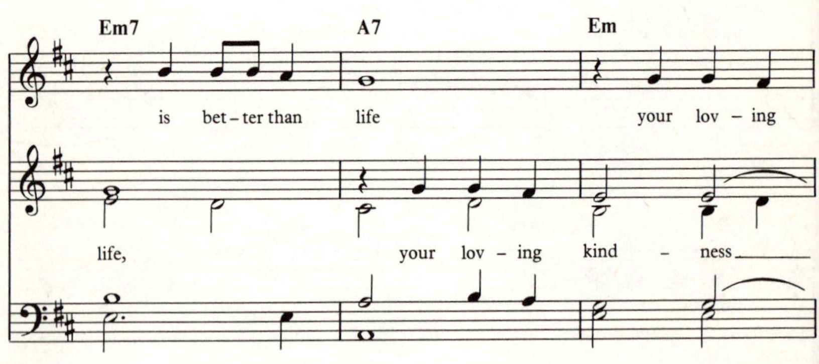
Em7
A7
Em
is bet – ter than life your lov – ing
life, your lov – ing kind – ness ___

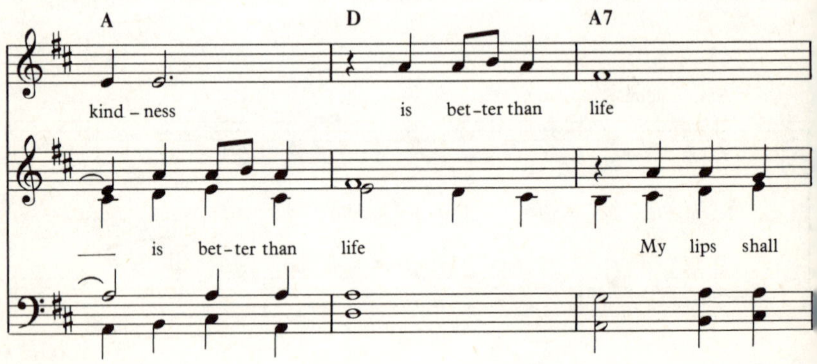
A
D
A7
kind – ness is bet-ter than life
___ is bet – ter than life My lips shall

D
D7
G
My lips shall praise you
So will I
praise you: So will I bless you
Em
D
Asus4
A7
D
bless you I will lift up my hands in your name.
I will lift up my hands in your name.

2 I lift my hands up in your name,
I lift my hands up in your name —
my lips shall praise you:
So will I bless you —
I will lift up my hands in your name.

54

ABBA FATHER

David Bilbrough
Arr. David Peacock

1st time only
2 & 3
Fine
Bb Eb F7 Bb Eb Cm F F7 Bb F F7 Bb
1. & 3. A-bba Fa-ther let me be yours and yours a-lone; 2. more your own.
may my will for e-ver be e - ver
3. yours a - lone
D. 𝄋 al Fine
D7 Gm D7 Gm Eb Cm7 F F7
Ne - ver let my heart grow cold, ne - ver let me go:

55

ALLELUIA, MY FATHER

Tim Cullen
Arr. David Peacock

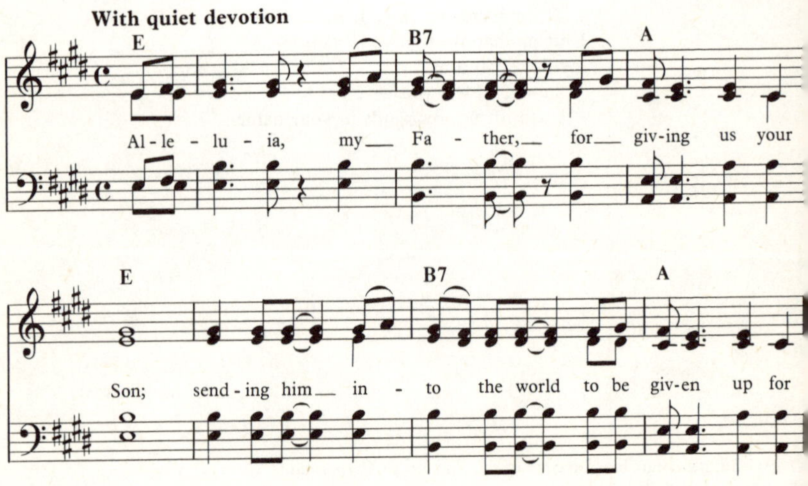
With quiet devotion
E B7 A
Al-le - lu - ia, my Fa - ther, for giv-ing us your
E B7 A
Son; send-ing him in - to the world to be giv-en up for

E A G♯m A E C♯m

men, know - ing we would bruise him and smite him from the

B7 E B7

earth: al - le - lu - ia, my Fa - ther, in his

A 1 E 2 E

death / life is my birth al - le life.

56

GOD IS SO GOOD

Unknown
Arr. David Peacock

E F♯m B7 F♯m B7 E E7 A E B7 E
1. God is so good, God is so good, God is so good, he's so good to me.

2 He took my sin,
he took my sin,
he took my sin:
he's so good to me.

3 Now I am free,
now I am free,
now I am free:
he's so good to me.

4 God is so good,
he took my sin,
now I am free:
he's so good to me.

57

HOLY, HOLY, HOLY, THE LORD GOD IS HOLY

Norman Warren

Descant Last Chorus only
C
Cmaj7
Am
E
Chorus
Ho - ly,
Ho - ly, ho - ly, ho - ly
A7
F♯m
Dm
A7
ho - - ly
the Lord God is ho - ly; his
Dm7
D°
Gsus4
G
1-2
glo - ry fills the world!
Gsus4
G
C
Last time
Fine
world! the world

THE FATHER
Choir
C
Cmaj7
Am
E
1. Touch me with the coal of fire;
2. Give me, Lord the word of God;
Accpt.
A7
F♯m
Dm
A7
touch me with the coal of fire, and
give me, Lord the word of God, for
Dm7
D°
Gsus4
G
to Chorus
purge a - way my sin:
here I am, send me:
to Chorus

58

HOW GREAT IS OUR GOD

Unknown
Arr. David Peacock

E F♯m B B7 E A

How great is our God, how great is his name.
He's the great-est one, for ev-er the same.

E B7 E E7 A D

He rolled back the wa-ters of the migh-ty Red Sea,

A Am6 E B7 E A E

And he said I'm go-ing to lead you put your trust in me.

59

I HAVE MADE A COVENANT

Karen Barrie
Arr. Norman Warren

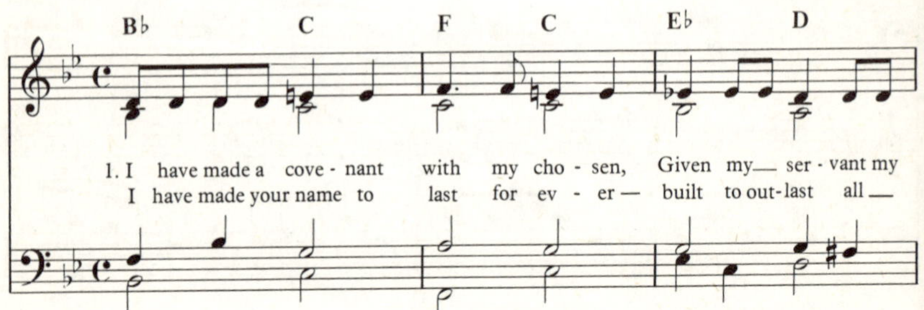
B♭ C F C E♭ D
1. I have made a cove-nant with my cho-sen, Given my ser-vant my
I have made your name to last for ev-er — built to out-last all

Gm
Chorus
G Bm G C D7
word,
time.
I will ce - le - brate your love for ev - er, Yah - weh;
G D7 G D G Bm
age on age my words pro-claim your love, For I claim that love is
Em Am D7 G C G D7 G
built to last for ev - er, Found-ed firm, your faith - ful - ness.

2 Yahweh, the assembly of those who love you
applaud your marvellous word:
who in the skies can compare with Yahweh,
who can rival him?
I will celebrate your love . . .

3 Happy the people who learn to acclaim you,
they rejoice in your light:
you are our glory and you are our courage,
our hope belongs to you.
I will celebrate your love . . .

4 I have revealed my chosen servant,
and he can rely on me;
giving him my love to last for ever,
he shall rise in my name.
I will celebrate your love . . .

5 He will call to me, my Father, my God,
for I make him my first-born Son;
I cannot take back my given promise
I've called him to shine like the sun.
I will celebrate your love . . .

60

I'M IN MY FATHER

Dave Rios
Arr. David Peacock

C
G
G7
Ladies:
I'm in my Fa - ther,
and my
Men:
I'm in my Fa - ther,
and my Fa-ther's in me;
Fa-ther's in me;
the Son and the Spi - rit
the Son and the Spi - rit
are all
C
F
C
G11
C
1st time only
2, 3
Fine
are all liv-ing in me
are all liv-ing in me.
liv- ing in me
liv-ing in me.
And

THE FATHER
F G7 C Dm G7 C C7
I'm liv-ing in them be cause I've been born a - gain; the
F G7 Em A7 D7 G
bless - ed tri-ni - ty has called me to their u - ni - ty.

61

LET GOD ARISE (Psalm 68:1)

E. Bacon
Arr. David Peacock

C G
Let God a - rise, his e - ne-mies be scat - ter - ed, let

C D7 G G7 C
God a-rise, his e-ne-mies be scattered, let God a - rise, his

C7 F Dm G7 C
e - ne-mies be scat-ter - ed, let God, let God a - rise.

62

MY GOD IS SO GREAT

Unknown
Arr. Norman Warren

Unison
G
Am7
D7
My God is so great, so strong, so migh-ty, there's no-thing that he can-not
1
2
C
do. My do. The ri-vers are his, the
mount-tains are his, the stars are his hand-i-work too. My
God is so great, so strong, so migh-ty, there's no-thing that he can-not do.

63

WE SEE THE LORD

Unknown
Arr. Norman Warren

F
we see Jesus
We see the Lord, we see the

C7 F Gm Gm7 C7 F C7 F
we see Jesus
Lord, and he is high and lift - ed up, and his train fills the tem-ple; He is

Gm Gm7 C C7 F B♭ F
high and lift - ed up, and his train fills the tem-ple; the an-gels cry 'Ho-ly', the

B♭ C7 F B♭ F
an-gels cry 'Ho - ly', the an-gels cry 'Ho - ly is the Lord!'

64

WHO MADE THE MOUNTAIN

Lange, Heath and Burke

Country n' Western
D Dmaj7 Bm F♯m A♭7 G D
v. 2
1. Who made the moun-tain, who made the trees___ Who made the ri - ver
2. Who made the flow - ers bloom in the spring_ Who writes the song for the
G A A7 Bm F♯m Gmaj7 G♯°
flow to the sea And who hung the moon in the star - ry sky?
ro - bin to sing And who sends the rain when the earth is dry?
D Bm G6 A G6 A7 D
v. 1
v. 2
Some - bo - dy big - ger than you and I you and I
Em A7 D A7 D G D D6
3. He lights the way when the road is long Keeps you com - pa - ny_______ with

THE FATHER
A F♯m A D6 Bm E7
love to guide you He walks be - side you just like he walks with
A7 D Dmaj7 Bm F♯m A♭7
me 4. When I am wea - ry fill - ed with des - pair,
G D G A7 Bm F♯m
Who gives me cour-age to go on from there? And who gives me faith that will
G G♯° D Bm G6 A7 D
ne - ver die? Some-bo - dy big - ger than you and I.

65

ALL THE WAY

M. Wilkinson
Arr. David Peacock

Gently
A A7 D Bm E7 A Bm
1. All the way, all the way, he came all the
A Dm7 Esus4 E7 A A7
way for me; all the way,
D Bm B7 A E7 A v. 2
all the way, he came all the way for me. 2. From

2 From heaven above to Bethlehem
he came all the way for me . . .

3 From Bethlehem to Jerusalem
he came all the way for me . . .

4 From Jerusalem to Calvary
he came all the way for me . . .

5 From Calvary to heaven above
he came all the way for me . . .

6 From heaven above into my heart
he came all the way for me . . .

7 Jesus came, Jesus came,
he came all the way for me . . .

66

COME AND PRAISE THE LORD OUR KING

Unknown
Arr. Norman Warren

D
G
Come and praise the Lord our king, al - le - lu - -

D
F♯m
G
A6
G6
D
A7
D
- ia, Come and praise the Lord our king, al - le - lu - ia.

1 Christ was born in Bethlehem, alleluia
Son of God and Son of Man: alleluia
Come and praise . . .

2 He grew up an earthly child, alleluia
of the world, but undefiled: alleluia
Come and praise . . .

3 Jesus died at Calvary, alleluia
rose again triumphantly! alleluia
Come and praise . . .

4 He will cleanse us from our sin, alleluia
if we live by faith in him: alleluia
Come and praise . . .

5 We will live with him one day, alleluia
and for ever with him stay: alleluia
Come and praise . . .

67

COMES MARY TO THE GRAVE

Words: Michael Perry
Music: Norman Warren

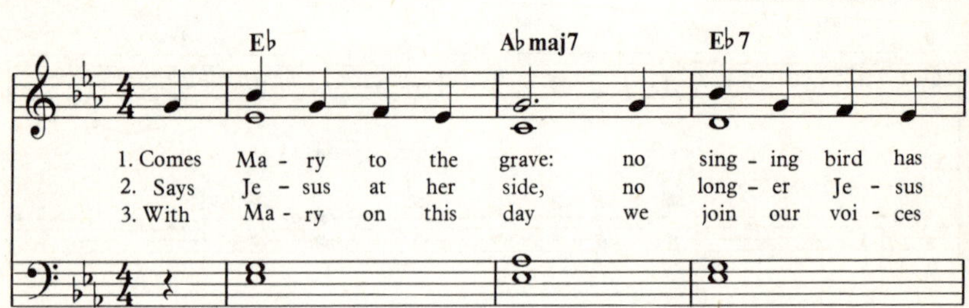
E♭
A♭maj7
E♭7
1. Comes Ma - ry to the grave: no sing - ing bird has
2. Says Je - sus at her side, no long - er Je - sus
3. With Ma - ry on this day we join our voi - ces

Fm
Gm7
Cm
A♭
spo - ken, nor has the world a wo - ken. And in her grief all
dy - ing 'Why Ma - ry are you cry - ing?' She turns, with joy, 'My
prais - ing the God of Je - sus' rais - ing, and sing the tri - umph

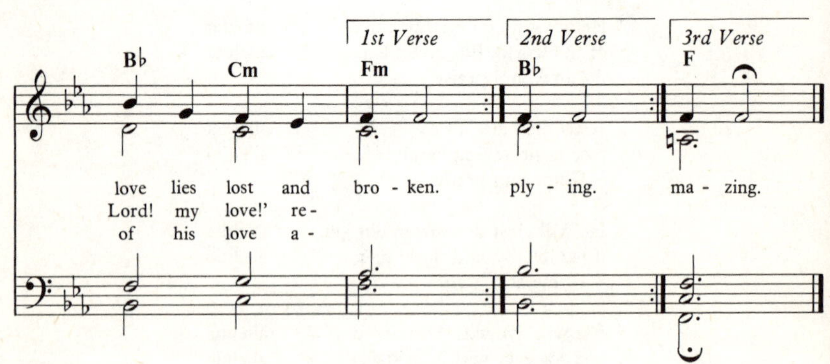
1st Verse
2nd Verse
3rd Verse
B♭
Cm
Fm
B♭
F
love lies lost and bro - ken.
Lord! my love!' re - ply - ing.
of his love a - ma - zing.

68

EMMANUEL, EMMANUEL

Words: Unknown
Arr. David Peacock

C
F
G7
C
Em - man - u - el,
Em - man - u - el,
A7
Dm
Dm7
G7
C
his name is called
Em - man - u - el.
F
G7
Em
God with us,
re - vealed in us,
A7
Dm
Dm7
G7
C
his name is called
Em - man - u - el.

69

GLORIOUS IN MAJESTY

Words: J. Cothram
Trad. Jewish Melody
Arr. D. Peacock

Dm C Dm C
1. Glo-ri-ous in maj-es-ty, ho-ly in his prais-es,
Bb Am Dm
Je-sus, our sa-viour, and our king
C Dm C
born a man, yet God of old: let us all a-dore him,
Bb Am Dm
filled with his spi-rit let us sing!
Chorus
F Am Dm Gm C Dm Gm Dm
Liv-ing is to love him, serv-ing him to know his free-dom!

C
B♭
Am
come a - long with us to join the praise of Je - sus,

Dm
C
B♭
C
Dm
come to Je - sus now, go to live his word re - joic - ing.

2 Victory he won for us,
freeing us from darkness,
dying and rising from the dead:
living with the Father now,
yet he is among us;
we are the body, he the head.
Living is to love him . . .

3 Brethren, we live in love,
living with each other;
gladly we share each other's pain:
yet he will not leave us so —
soon he is returning,
taking us back with him to reign.
Living is to love him . . .

70

HE IS LORD

Unknown
Arr. Norman Warren

(Capo I) Gently
A E7 A A7 D G D Dmaj7
He is Lord, he is Lord, he is
Bm Bm7 E E7 A A11 D
ris-en from the dead, and he is Lord! Ev-ery knee shall
D7 G Em D A7 D G6 D
bow, ev-ery tongue con - fess that Je - sus Christ is Lord.
Angela Reith
Descant
(He is Lord) He is Lord, he is Lord, he is
ris-en from the dead and he is Lord! ev-ery knee, ev-ery
knee shall bow, tongue con - fess that Je - sus Christ is Lord.

71

HE IS MY SAVIOUR

Keith Routledge
Arr. David Peacock

Slowly
Eb
C7
Fm
1. He is my sa-viour and my friend and I live my life for
Bb7
Eb
Eb7
Ab
Abm
him; he's all I need from day to day, he
1,2
Last Verse
Eb
Cm
Fm7
Bb7
Fm7
Bb11
Eb
is the truth, the life, the way. truth, the life, the way.

2 When you give yourself to him,
he makes everything worthwhile;
he'll be all you need from day to day —
he is the truth, the life, the way.

3 Why don't you let him be your friend
and your saviour and your God?
He's all you need from day to day —
he is the truth, the truth, the life, the way.

72

HE IS THE WAY

Words and Music: G. Brattle

Not too slowly
D C♯ D Em A7 D6 D
1. He is the way — the end of all my search - ing;
2. More of the way — dear Lord, be this my choos - ing;
F♯m C♯m F♯m Dm6 A E7 A A7
he is the truth — I'll trust his ev - ery word;
more of the truth — Lord, teach me day by day;
Bm D+ Em F♯m E°
he is the life — a - bun - dant, ev - er - last - ing:
more of the life — for - ev - er sat - is - fy - ing:
Bm Am7 F♯m Em G Em6 Bm Em7 A6 D
this is the Christ, the sa - viour of the world!
more of your - self — the life, the truth, the way!

73

HIGHER THAN THE HILLS

Words and Music: Norman J. Clayton

F Bb F A Dm
High - er than the hills, deep - er than the sea,
Bb Gm7 C C7 F° F
broad - er than the skies a - bove is my re - deem - er's love for me;
F Bb F A Dm F7
to his cross of shame, Je - sus free - ly came,
Gm B♮° F D7 Gm C6 F
bear - ing all my sin and sor - row — won - drous love!

74

HIS NAME IS HIGHER

Unknown
Arr. Norman Warren

D7 G D

His name is high - er than an - y oth - er

A 1 D

his name is Je - sus, his name is Lord;

2 A D G D D7

his name is Lord. His name is

G D

won - der - ful, his name is coun - sel - lor,

THE LORD JESUS CHRIST
A
his name is Prince of Peace, the migh - ty
D D7 G
God; his name is high - er
D
than an - y oth - er, his name is
A A7 D G D
Je - sus, his name is Lord.

75

HIS NAME IS WONDERFUL

Unknown
Arr. Norman Warren

F
D7
His name is won - der - ful, his name is
He is the migh - ty king, mas - ter of
Gm
C7
F
won - der - ful,
ev - ery - thing,
his name is won - der - ful,
1
2
G7
C7
C7
F
Je - sus my Lord;
Je - sus my Lord.
C7
F
C7
F
He's the great shep - herd, the rock of all a - ges,

G7
C
C7
al - migh - ty God is he;

F
D7
Gm
bow down be - fore him, love and a - dore him,

C7
F
C7
F
his name is won - der - ful, Je - sus my Lord!

76

HOW LOVELY ON THE MOUNTAINS

Lenny Smith
Arr. Norman Warren

C F Dm G7 F C
How love - ly on the moun - tains are the feet of him
A7 Dm G G7 C F
who brings good news, good news!
C F Dm G7 F C
an - nounc - ing peace, pro - claim - ing news of hap - pi - ness:
A7 Dm G G7 C
Our God reigns, our God reigns,
(Alt. V.) Saying to Zion: your God reigns.

THE LORD JESUS CHRIST

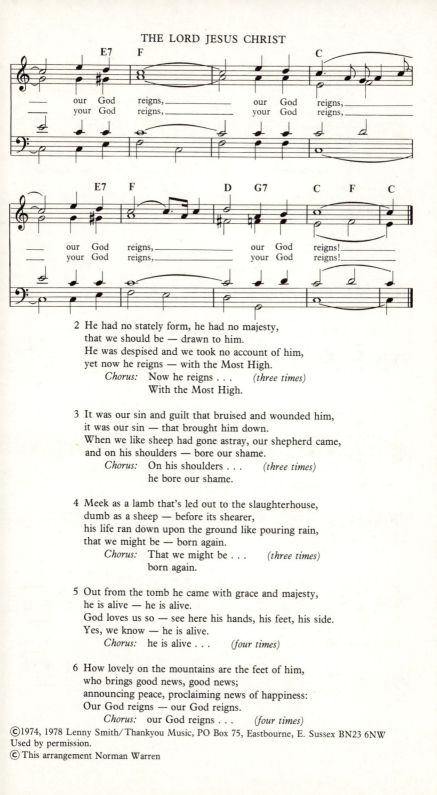

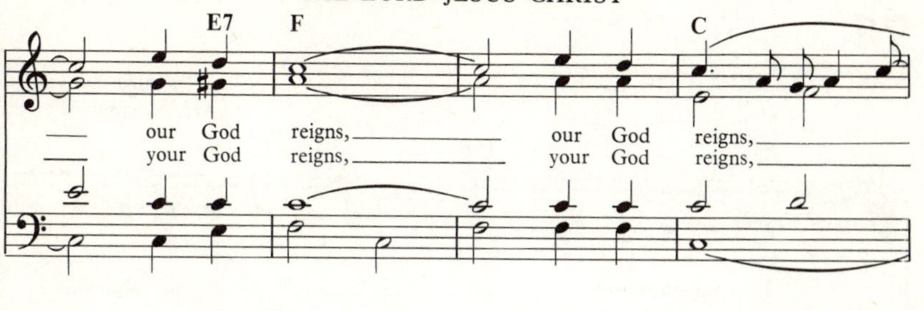
E7
F
C
our God reigns,
your God reigns,
our God reigns,
your God reigns,

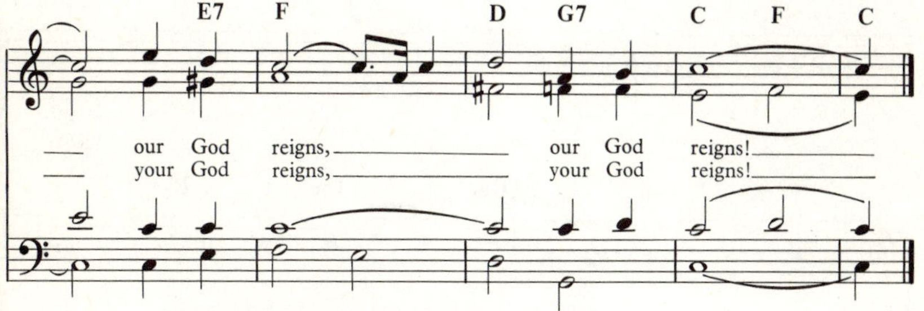
E7
F
D
G7
C
F
C
our God reigns,
your God reigns,
our God reigns!
your God reigns!

2 He had no stately form, he had no majesty,
that we should be — drawn to him.
He was despised and we took no account of him,
yet now he reigns — with the Most High.
Chorus: Now he reigns . . . *(three times)*
With the Most High.

3 It was our sin and guilt that bruised and wounded him,
it was our sin — that brought him down.
When we like sheep had gone astray, our shepherd came,
and on his shoulders — bore our shame.
Chorus: On his shoulders . . . *(three times)*
he bore our shame.

4 Meek as a lamb that's led out to the slaughterhouse,
dumb as a sheep — before its shearer,
his life ran down upon the ground like pouring rain,
that we might be — born again.
Chorus: That we might be . . . *(three times)*
born again.

5 Out from the tomb he came with grace and majesty,
he is alive — he is alive.
God loves us so — see here his hands, his feet, his side.
Yes, we know — he is alive.
Chorus: he is alive . . . *(four times)*

6 How lovely on the mountains are the feet of him,
who brings good news, good news;
announcing peace, proclaiming news of happiness:
Our God reigns — our God reigns.
Chorus: our God reigns . . . *(four times)*

77

I AM THE BREAD OF LIFE

S. Suzanne Toolan
Arr. Norman Warren

Bb
Dm
Eb
1. I am the bread of life: he who comes to me shall not
F
Gm
Dm7
Eb
hun - ger, he who be - lieves in me shall not thirst;
Bb
Eb
Cm
No one can come to me un - less the Fa - ther
F
Chorus
Bb
F
Bb
draw him: and I will raise him up, and I will

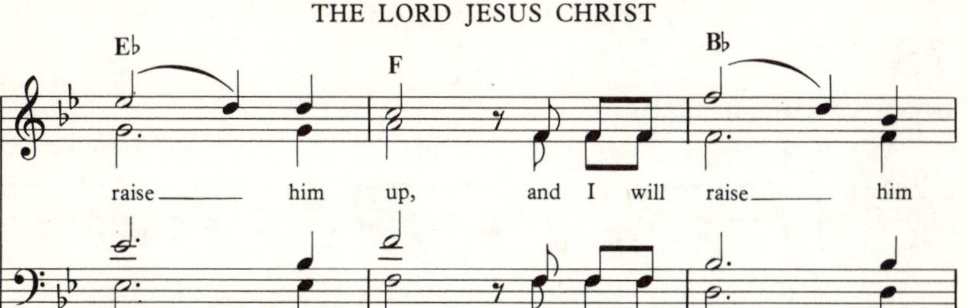
E♭
F
B♭
raise ___ him up, and I will raise ___ him

E♭
B♭
F7
1, 4
B♭
5
B♭
up ___ on the last ___ day. 2. The day.
3. Un –

2 The bread that I will give, is my flesh for the life of the world,
and he who eats of this bread, he shall live for ever,
he shall live for ever:
And I will raise him up . . .

3 Unless you eat of the flesh of the Son of Man
and drink of his blood, and drink of his blood,
you shall not have life within you:
And I will raise him up . . .

4 I am the resurrection, I am the life;
he who believes in me, even if he die,
he shall live for ever:
And I will raise him up . . .

5 Yes Lord, we believe
that you are the Christ, the Son of God
who has come into the world:
And you will raise us up, and you will raise us up,
and you will raise us up on the last day.

78

IN THE NAME OF JESUS

Unknown
Arr. David Peacock

E B7 E B7 E
In the name of Je - sus, in the name of Je - sus we have the vic - to -
F♯m B7 F♯m B7 F♯m B7
- ry; in the name of Je - sus, in the name of Je - sus,
E E7 A B7
Al - le-lu - ia
Sa-tan will have to flee. Who can tell what
E C♯7 F♯m B7 E E7
God can do; who can tell of his love for you?
A B7 G♯m C♯7 F♯m B7 E
In the name of Je - sus, Je - sus, we have the vic - to - ry.

79

JESUS CHRIST IS RISEN TODAY

Music: Sue Gilmurray

Introduction
Unison
E G♯m A B7 E G♯m A B7 E G♯m
1. Je-sus Christ is
A B7 E G♯m A B7 C♯m G♯m
risen to-day, a - lle - lu - ia our tri-um-phant ho-ly day;
A B7 E C♯m A
a - lle - lu - ia who did once up - on the cross, suf - fer to re-
B7 G♯m A E A E G♯m E
1,2
3
- deem our loss. A - - lle - lu - ia. - ia.

2 Hymns of praise then let us sing alleluia
now to Christ our heavenly king! —alleluia
who endured the cross and grave
sinners to redeem and save. alleluia

3 But the pains which he endured alleluia
our salvation have procured; alleluia
now beyond the sky he's king
where the angels ever sing. alleluia

80

JESUS CHRIST, ONE WITH GOD

Words: Margaret Bowdler
Music: Dvořák
Arr. Norman Warren

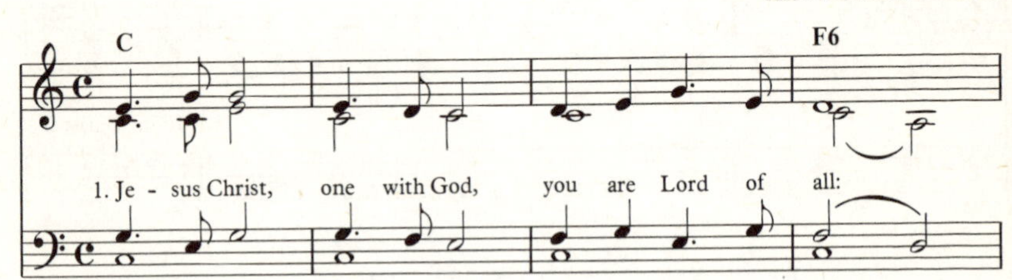
C
F6
1. Je - sus Christ, one with God, you are Lord of all:

C
Am
Dm
G7
C
in this vast un - i - verse man seems ve - ry small.

F
G7
F
Can it be, he whose works all the heav - ens span,

v. 1, 2
C
Am
Dm
G7
C
can look down lov - ing - ly, care for mere man?

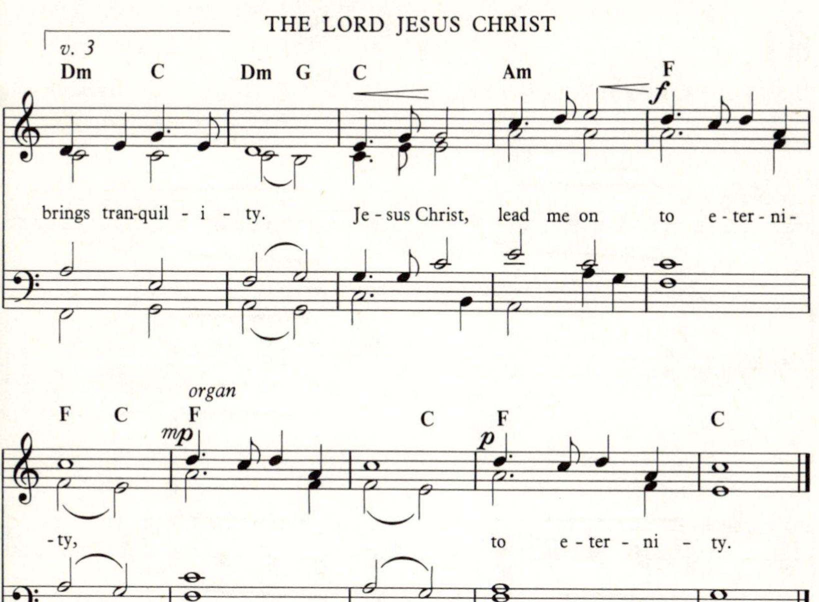
v. 3
Dm C Dm G C Am F
f
brings tran-quil - i - ty. Je - sus Christ, lead me on to e - ter - ni -
organ
F C F C F C
mp
p
- ty, to e - ter - ni - ty.

2 Love of God, shown to man
by his only Son:
through his life and his death
our salvation won.
Love of God fill my life
that I may serve you,
telling all of the love
shown on Calvary!

3 Peace of God, passing all
man can comprehend,
fill my heart, calm my fears,
keep me to the end!
Fear and strife, war and want
all around I see:
only Christ, prince of peace,
brings tranquility.

Jesus Christ, lead me on
to eternity . . .
to eternity!

81

JESUS HOW LOVELY YOU ARE

David Bolton

E F♯m B E
p
Je - sus, how love - ly you are!
C♯m F♯m B E
You are so gen - tle so pure and kind,
E F♯m B E
you shine like the morn - ing star:
C♯m F♯m B E
Fine
Je - sus how love - ly you are.

THE LORD JESUS CHRIST

Verse
mf
E A/C♯ B7 E E/G♯ A
1. Al - le - lu - ia, Je - sus is my Lord and (my
Bsus E A/C♯ E/B A
Lord and king)
king Al - le - lu - ia, Je - sus is
E/G♯ A Bsus D.C.
(my eve - ry - thing.)
my eve - ry - thing.

2 Alleluia, Jesus died and rose again;
alleluia, Jesus forgave all my sin.
Jesus, how lovely you are . . !

3 Alleluia, Jesus is meek and lowly;
alleluia, Jesus is pure and holy.
Jesus, how lovely you are . . !

4 Alleluia, Jesus is the bridegroom;
alleluia, Jesus will take his bride soon.
Jesus, how lovely you are . . !

82

JESUS I WORSHIP YOU

Norman Warren

B♭
E♭
Cm
F7
1. Je - sus I wor-ship you, Je - sus I wor-ship you,
B♭
E♭
F7
B♭
Je - sus I wor-ship you, Son of God:
D7
Gm
C7
F7
You came from heaven a-bove to bring the Fa-ther's love
B♭
E♭
F7
B♭
Je - sus I wor-ship you, Son of God!

2 Jesus I trust in you,
Jesus I trust in you,
Jesus I trust in you,
Son of God:
You died on Calvary
to set my spirit free,
Jesus I trust in you,
Son of God!

3 Jesus I feed on you,
Jesus I feed on you,
Jesus I feed on you,
Son of God:
You are the living bread,
you meet my every need,
Jesus I feed on you,
Son of God!

4 Jesus I love you,
Jesus I love you,
Jesus I love you,
Son of God:
I give my self to you,
lay down my life for you,
Jesus I love you,
Son of God!

83

JESUS IS LORD ALLELUIA

Philip Moore
Arr. David Peacock

Fairly slow, but flowing

1. D
Em
A7
D
Em
A7
D
1. Je-sus is
Lord, Je-sus is
Lord,
al - le - lu
ia!
Je-sus is

Em
A7
D
Em
A7
D
2.
Em
A7
D
Lord, Je-sus is Lord,
al - le - lu - ia!
Al - le - lu - ia,
al -

Em
A7
D
Em
A7
D
Em
A7
D
- le - lu - ia,
al - le - lu - ia
al - le - lu - ia.

This may be sung as a round.

84

JESUS IS THE NAME WE WORSHIP

Words: Diana Brand
Music: Alan Durden

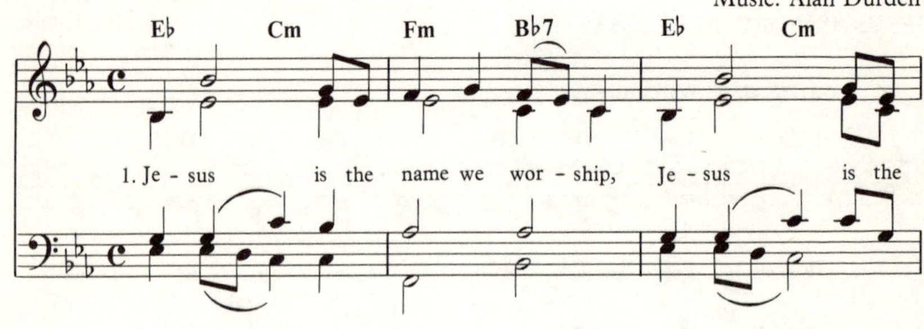
Eb Cm Fm Bb7 Eb Cm
1. Je - sus is the name we wor - ship, Je - sus is the

Fm Bb7 Eb7 Ab Gm Cm
Friend we love Je - sus is our Lord and Sa - viour

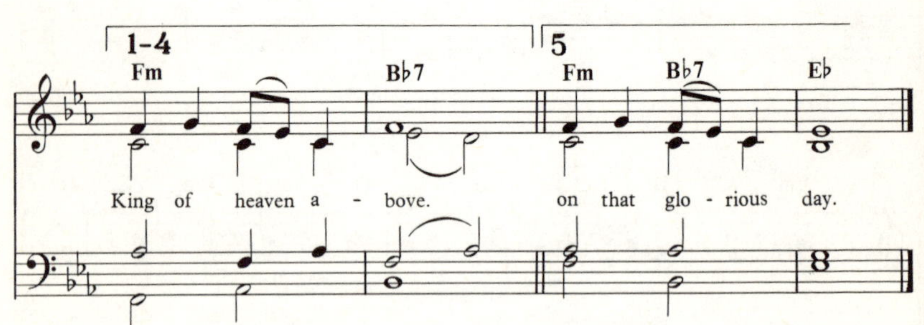
1-4 5
Fm Bb7 Fm Bb7 Eb
King of heaven a - bove. on that glo - rious day.

2 Jesus knows when we are troubled,
Jesus hears our every prayer,
Jesus has our trials and sorrows
always in his care.

3 Jesus made the lame go walking,
Jesus made the blind to see,
Jesus healed the sick and wounded:
wondrous, O was he!

4 Jesus is our great redeemer,
Jesus died for you and me,
Jesus took our sins and failings,
bore them on the Tree.

5 Jesus lives within us daily,
Jesus in our hearts will stay
till we meet with him in heaven
on that glorious day.

85

JESUS, JESUS, JESUS, SWEETEST NAME ON EARTH

A. Paget Wilkes

G
C
Am
D7
1. Je - sus, Je - sus, Je - sus! sweet-est name on earth:
G
E7
Am
D7
G
how can I, a sin - ner, come to know its worth?
Alternative tune
1. Je - sus, Je - sus, Je - sus! sweet-est name on earth:
how can I, a sin - ner, come to know its worth?

Words: A. Paget Wilkes
Music: C. Hudson

2 O the sinful sorrow,
O the strangest shame,
that I saw no beauty
in that sacred name:

3 Never found the mystery
in that simple word,
Jesus, Jesus, Jesus —
saviour, friend and Lord!

4 Jesus, Jesus, Jesus!
loved me in my shame:
O the joy and wonder
in that sacred name!

86

JESUS, JESUS, JESUS YOUR LOVE

C. Bowater
Arr. D. Peacock

A E F♯m D A
Je - sus, Je - sus, Je - - sus, your love has
Esus4 E7 A Dmaj7 Esus4 E A E
melt - ed my heart; Je - sus, Je - sus,
F♯m Bm E7 A D E7 D A
Je - - sus, your love has melt - ed my heart.

87

JESUS, JESUS

Unknown
Arr. Norman Warren

Em Bm Em Bm7 Em Bm Em Bm

1. Je - sus, Je - sus, 2. Let me tell you what I know!

Em Bm Em Bm7 Em Bm7 Em
3.
4.
you have giv - en us your Spi - rit; We love you so.

Alternative verses line 3
You have given us your Life, Love, Glory, Riches, etc.

This may also be sung as an unaccompanied Round

88

JESUS' LOVE IS VERY WONDERFUL

Words: H. W. Rattle
Music: Trad.
Arr. Norman Warren

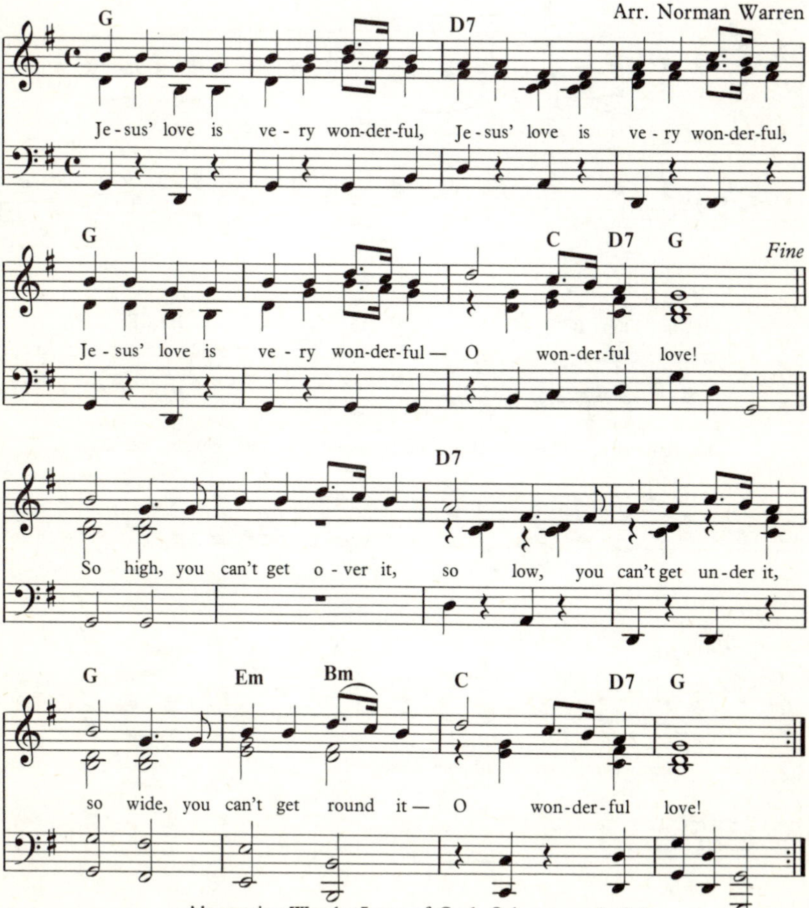

Je - sus' love is ve - ry won-der-ful, Je - sus' love is ve - ry won-der-ful,
Je - sus' love is ve - ry won-der-ful — O won-der-ful love!
So high, you can't get o - ver it, so low, you can't get un-der it,
so wide, you can't get round it — O won-der-ful love!

Alternative Words: Love of God, O how wonderful

89

JESUS MY SAVIOUR

Robert Stoodley

Slowly flowing and reflective
E B7 E B7 E F♯m
Je-sus my sav-iour, O how I love you, for you have filled me
E A6 B A E B
with your new life; all your heav'n-ly glo - ry
C♯m F♯m B7 E A6 E A6 B7 E
you count-ed as noth-ing and bore the pain of death to make us free:
mp B E A C♯7 F♯m
cresc. mf
There - fore with all my heart I'll glad - ly sing your praise

B7 E C♯m F♯m E A B7 E B7
and do so all my days to bless your ho-ly name, for God has exalted you,
E F♯ B7 E A6 E A6 B7 Fine E
seat-ed at the Fa-ther's side: you shall be glo-ri-fied, Je-sus our king. (D.S.)
Fine

90

Words: Naida Hearn
Music: Patricia Cain
Arr. David Peacock

JESUS, NAME ABOVE ALL NAMES

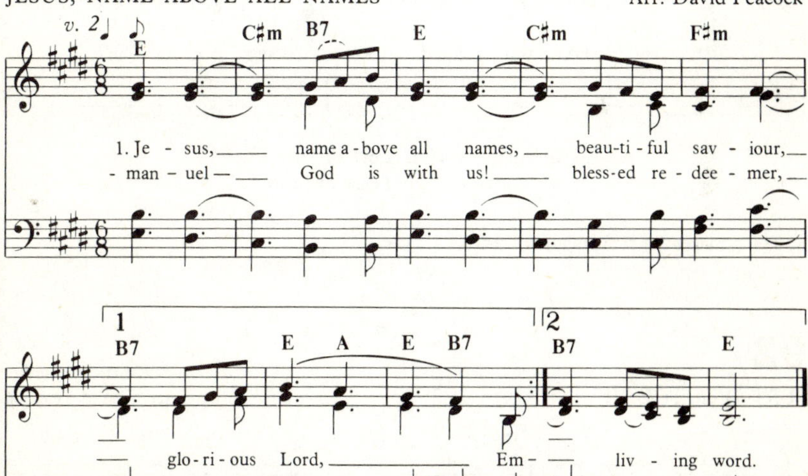
v. 2
E C♯m B7 E C♯m F♯m
1. Je - sus, name a-bove all names, beau-ti-ful sav - iour,
- man - uel — God is with us! bless-ed re - dee - mer,
1 B7 E A E B7 2 B7 E
glo-ri-ous Lord, Em- liv - ing word.

2 Jesus, bearer of my sins,
beautiful saviour, glorious Lord,
you suffered giving me freedom:
living redeemer, you are my Lord!

3 Jesus, name above all names,
suffering servant, faithful friend
good shepherd, risen master,
king of glory, Lord of all!

91

JOY OF JESUS

Anon
Arr. Norman Warren

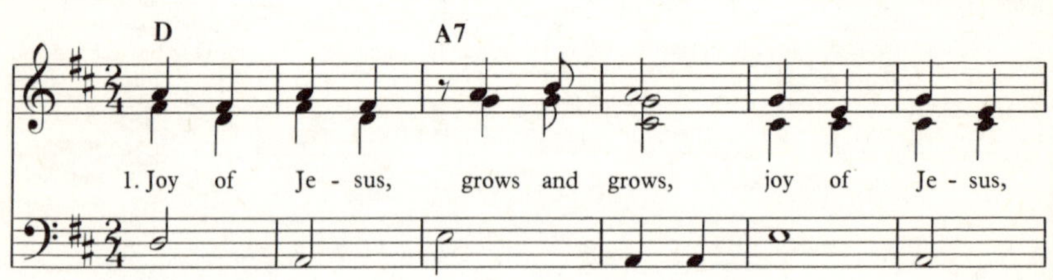
D
A7
1. Joy of Je - sus, grows and grows, joy of Je - sus,

D
D7
o - ver - flows, joy of Je - sus, makes my spi - rit

G
D
G
A7
D
free, thank you Lord, for giv - ing it to me!

Alternative verses: Love of Jesus . . .
Peace of Jesus . . .

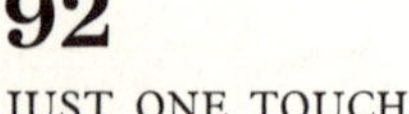

92

JUST ONE TOUCH

Keith Routledge
Arr. David Peacock

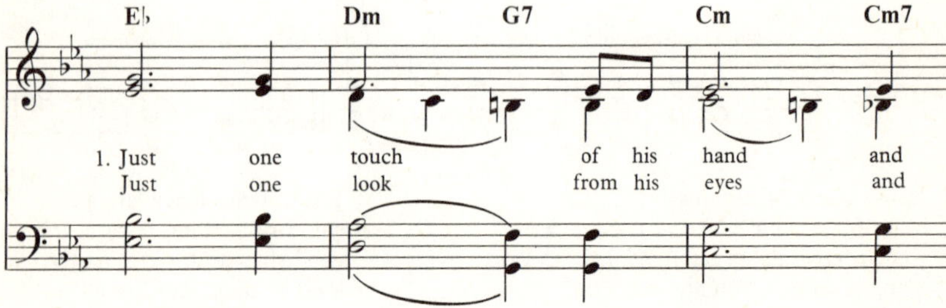
E♭
Dm
G7
Cm
Cm7
1. Just one touch of his hand and
Just one look from his eyes and

THE LORD JESUS CHRIST

3rd time to ⊕ Coda
B♭m7 E♭7 A♭ Gm
1
Fm B♭7
you ___ will un - der - stand what Je - sus ___ can do for
you ___ will re - al - ize what
E♭ B♭7
you: ___
2
Fm B♭7 E♭ A♭
Je - sus can do for you. 2. Just one
A♭♮5 A♭6 A♭7 Gm7 C7
word it's his voice you heard then you'll know peace of
D.C. al Coda ⊕ CODA
Fm7 Cm Fm7 B♭7 Fm7 B♭7
mind with Je - sus in your heart: ___ Je - sus ___ can do for
Gm7 C7 Fm7 B♭7 D♭7 E♭6
you, ___ what Je - sus ___ can do for you.

93

LORD JESUS

Paul Goodwin
Arr. Norman Warren

Gently, not too slowly
Introduction
Chorus
E B7 E A E B7 E
Lord Je-sus, Lord
F♯m G♯m A E
Je - sus, what a won - der you are, you are brigh-ter than the
A E F♯m B E F♯m
morn - ing star; You are fair - er, much fair - er than the
G♯m A A6 E B B7
li - lies that grow by the way side, pre - cious, more pre - cious than

THE LORD JESUS CHRIST

Verse
E A E E7 A F♯m
gold.
1. You're like the rose of Sha - ron the
2. You are the King of glo - ry, the

G♯m C♯m G♯m A E
fair - est of the fair; you are all my heart could e'er de -
sun of right-eous - ness, and your beau - ty shines up - on our

F♯m B7 E F♯m E
- sire.
lives.
Lord Je - sus, Lord Je - sus, what a won - der you

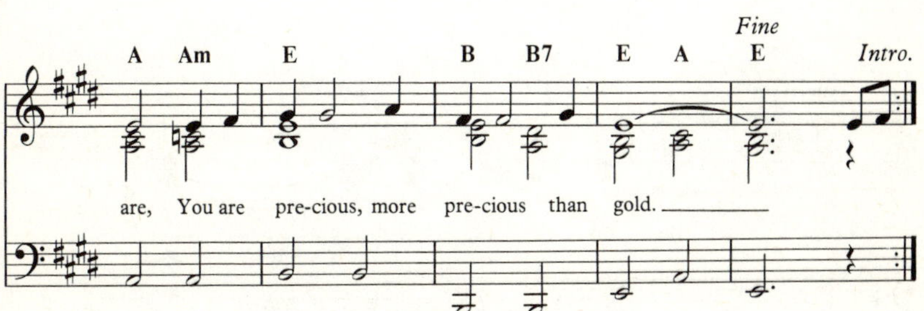
A Am E B B7 E A Fine E Intro.
are, You are pre - cious, more pre - cious than gold.

94

Words: Laura Winnen
Music: Jeff Cothran

MY LORD, HE IS A-COMING SOON

Capo 2 **(Dm)**

With a slow 'blues' swing: one beat to a bar

Refrain

Em(Dm)
*Em♯7(Dm♯7)
*Em7(Dm7)
*Em6(Dm6)
My Lord, he is a com - ing soon pre-

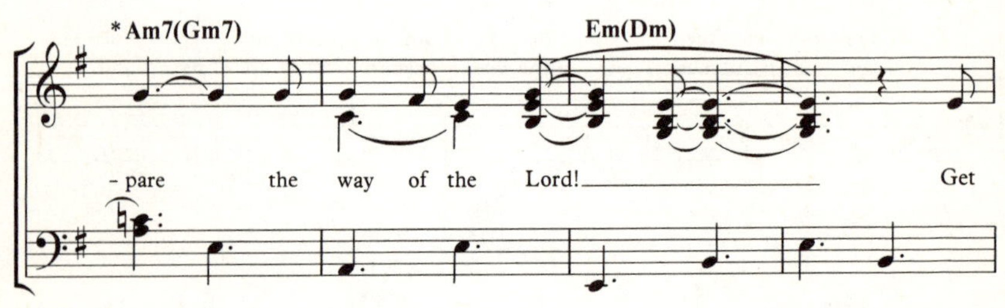
*Am7(Gm7)
Em(Dm)
- pare the way of the Lord! Get

Em♯7(Dm♯7)
Em7(Dm7)
Em6(Dm6)
ev - ery thing rea - dy for that day: pre -

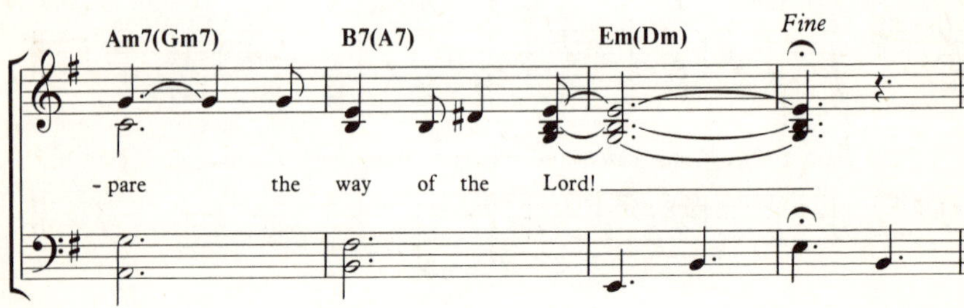
Am7(Gm7)
B7(A7)
Em(Dm)
Fine
- pare the way of the Lord!

THE LORD JESUS CHRIST

Am7(Gm7) Em(Dm)

1. If you're a - sleep ___ it's time to wake up: ___ a -
2. Come, Lord ___ Je - sus, come in - to my heart: ___ pre -

Am7(Gm7) Em(Dm)

- wake, O ___ sleep - er, a - rise! ___ If
- pare the way of the king! ___

Am7(Gm7) Em(Dm) Am(Gm)

you're in the dark, ___ it's time to be lit: ___ a - wake, O
He is ___ com - ing, he's com - ing soon: ___ pre - pare the

B(A)
B7(A7)
D.C.
sleep - er, a rise! ___
way of the king! ___

*Em♯7 (Dm♯7) Em7 (Dm7) Em6 (Dm6) Am7 (Gm7)

95

MY PEACE

Keith Routledge
Arr. David Peacock

C Am7 Dm7 G G7 C Am7

My peace I give unto you: it's a peace that the world cannot

Dm7 G G7 F Em7 Am Dm

give, it's a peace that the world cannot un-der-stand; peace to

G Em Em7 Am Dm G G7 C

know, peace to live — my peace I give un-to you.

Alternative Verses: My joy . . .
My love . . .

96

NOTHING BUT THE LOVE OF JESUS

Keith Routledge
Arr. D. Peacock

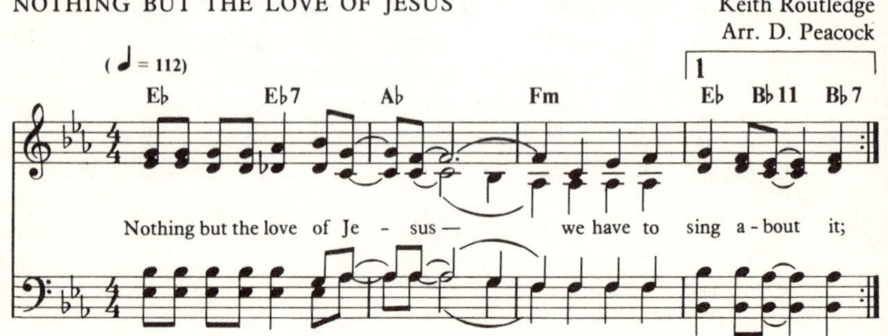
(♩ = 112)
1
E♭ E♭7 A♭ Fm E♭ B♭11 B♭7
Nothing but the love of Je - sus — we have to sing a-bout it;

THE LORD JESUS CHRIST

2
Eb Eb7 Ab Gm C7
talk a – bout it! No-thing but the love of Je – sus
Fm Bb7 Eb7 Ab D7
is chang – ing the way we live;_ no-thing but the love of Je –
Gm C7 Fm F Bb7 Cm Fm F
– sus,_ his good news of peace and joy — that's all we've got to
Bbsus4 Bb (Unison) Eb Cm
give. Do you know
love
Fm Bb11 Eb Cm Fm7 Bb11 Fine
do you know him? Do you
do you love him?

Alternative verse: Nothing but the *Power* of Jesus . . . etc.

97

NOW THE GREEN BLADE RISES

Words: J. M. C. Crum
Music: Trad.
Arr. Norman Warren

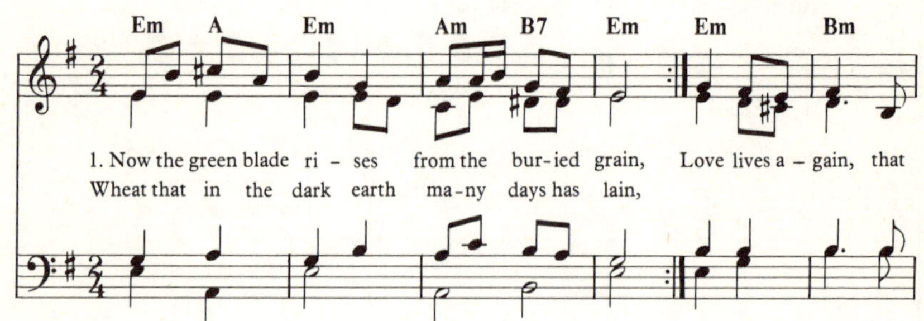
Em A Em Am B7 Em Em Bm
1. Now the green blade ri - ses from the bur-ied grain, Love lives a - gain, that
Wheat that in the dark earth ma-ny days has lain,

Em Bm Em A Em Am B7 Em
with the dead has been, Love is come a - gain, like wheat that springs green.

2 In the grave they laid him, Love whom men had slain,
thinking that never he would wake again;
laid in the earth like grain that sleeps unseen —
Love is come again, like wheat that springs green.

3 Forth he came at Easter, like the risen grain,
he that for three days in the grave had lain;
live from the dead my risen Lord is seen —
Love is come again, like wheat that springs green.

4 When our hearts are wintry, grieving or in pain,
your touch can call us back to life again;
fields of our hearts that dead and bare have been —
Love is come again, like wheat that springs green.

98

O THE BLOOD OF JESUS

Anon
Arr. Norman Warren

G
C
G
D7
Gsus4
G
D7
Em
1. O the blood of Je - sus, O the blood of Je - sus,

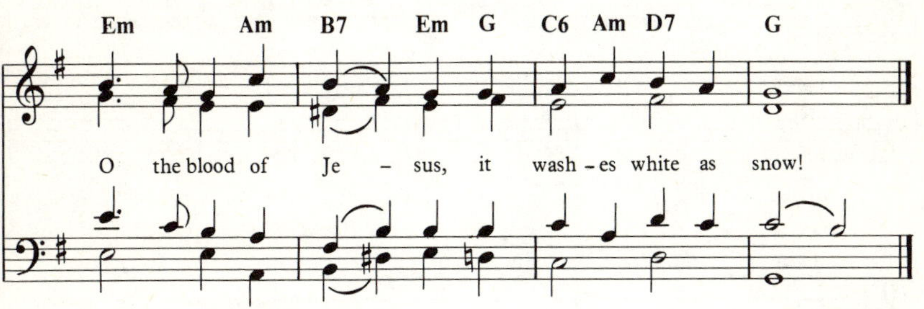
Em
Am
B7
Em
G
C6
Am
D7
G
O the blood of Je - sus, it wash - es white as snow!

2 O the word of Jesus,
O the word of Jesus,
O the word of Jesus,
it cleanses white as snow!

3 O the love of Jesus,
O the love of Jesus,
O the love of Jesus,
it makes my body whole!

99

O WHAT A GIFT

Pat Uhl Howard
Arr. Norman Warren

Brightly
Chorus
Bm F♯m Bm Em
O what a gift! what a won-der-ful gift! Who can tell the won-ders of the
Bm A Bm
Lord? Let us o – pen our eyes and our ears and our hearts; It is
F♯m F♯m7 Fine Bm
Christ the Lord it is he!
p Verse
1. In the still-ness of the night when the
Am G F♯m
world was a-sleep, the al – might – y word leapt out.
Bm Am G F♯m
He came to Ma – ry, he came to us, Christ came to the land of Gali –

Bm
F♯m
F♯m7
Bm
lee.
Christ our Lord and our king.
Descant
A. Reith
O what a gift what a won-der-ful gift who can
tell the won-ders of the Lord? Let us op – en our eyes, our
ears and our hearts, it is Christ the Lord, it is he!

2 On the night before he died —
it was Passover night
and he gathered his friends together.
He broke the bread, he blessed the wine;
it was the gift of his love and his life.
Christ our Lord and our king!
O what a gift . . !

3 On the hill of Calvary
while the world held its breath,
it was there for us all to see;
God gave his Son, his only Son,
for the love of you and me —
Christ our Lord and our king!
O what a gift . . !

4 It was early on that morning
when the guards were asleep,
back to life came he!
He conquered death, he conquered sin —
but victory he gave to you and me,
Christ our Lord and our king!
O what a gift . . !

5 Some day with the saints
we will come before our Father,
and then we will shout and dance and sing!
For in our midst for our eyes to see
will be Christ our Lord and our king,
Christ our Lord and our king!
O what a gift . . !

100

ON CALVARY'S TREE

Words: A. W. Edsor
Music (melody): A. E. Walton
Arr. Norman Warren

E (Emaj7) C♯m F♯m F♯m7 B B7
On Calva - ry's tree he died for me,

C♯m F♯m F♯ B B7 E (Emaj7) C♯m
that I his love might know; to set me free

F♯m B7 C♯m F♯m B7 E
he died for me that's why I love him so.

101

PRECIOUS JESUS

Trad. Polish Song
Words: Roy Tanner
Arr. Norman Warren

G Am6 G C G C D7
Pre - cious Je - sus, Pre - cious Je - sus, you have brought us back from

THE LORD JESUS CHRIST

G D7 G C D7 C D7 G C
death; Through your love you made us new Lord And we
G C D7 G C Am
thank you most of all. You are King Lord, Prince of
D Bm Em C D G C
Peace Lord, Liv - ing Sa - viour great Re - deem - er O
G C D7 Em G C D7 G
how we love_ you O_ how we love_ you.

102

SEE HIM LIKE A GAZELLE

Hugh Pollock
Arr. Norman Warren

Gently
D Dm7 Gmaj7 G6 A7
1. See him like a ga - zelle leap - ing o - ver the

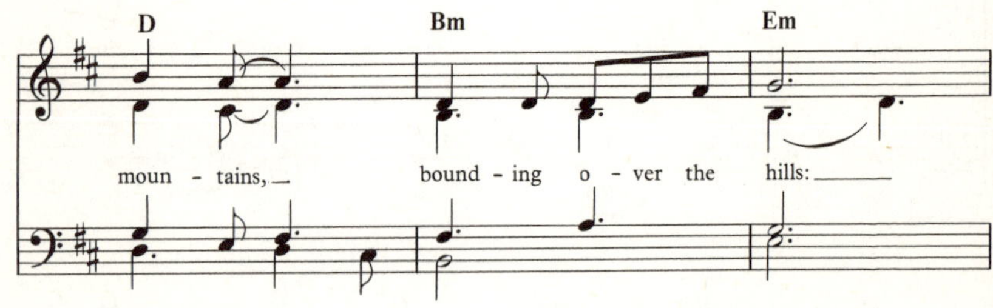
D Bm Em
moun - tains, bound - ing o - ver the hills:

A7 D Bm
My be - loved one comes! Tur - tle doves sing in the

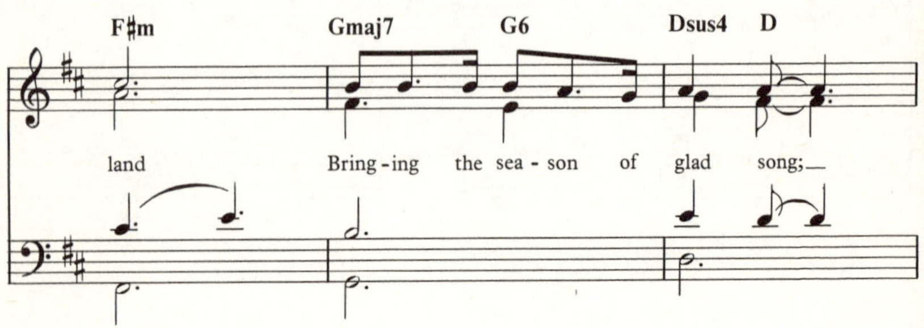
F♯m Gmaj7 G6 Dsus4 D
land Bring - ing the sea - son of glad song;

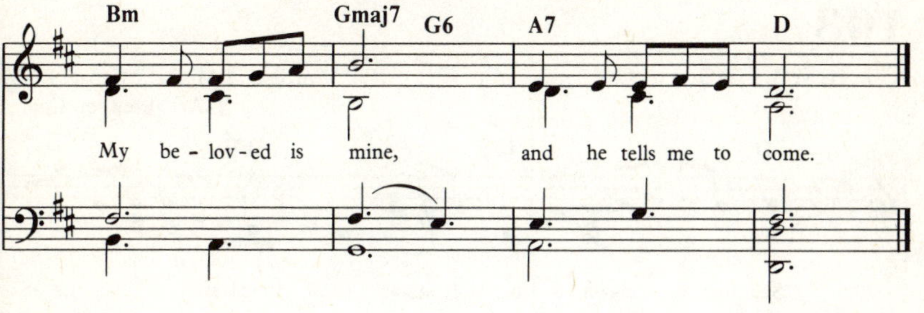
Bm
Gmaj7
G6
A7
D
My be - lov - ed is mine, and he tells me to come.

2 Hear him lifting his voice —
such a sweet invitation,
see him stand by my side:
my beloved One comes!
Turtledoves sing . . .

3 First figs seen on the tree —
blossom of vine gives its fragrance,
vineyards bursting in flower:
my beloved One comes!
Turtledoves sing . . .

4 See, the winter is past,
rain is over and gone now,
flowers appear on the earth:
my beloved One comes!
Turtledoves sing . . .

103

SEE HIM LYING

Words and Music: Michael Perry
Arr. Stephen Coates

D
G
A7
1. See him ly - ing on a bed of straw; A draugh-ty sta - ble with an
D
A7
D
G
o - pen door; Ma - ry cra - dling the babe she bore The
A7
D
D7
Chorus
G
prince of glo - ry is his name. O now car - ry me to
D
A7
D
A7
Beth - le - hem To see the Lord ap - pear to men;

Small notes optional ending for last verse
D
B7
Em
A7
Just as poor as was the stable then, the prince of glo-ry when he
D
Gm
Verses 1–3
D
Gm
Verse 4
D
came.

2 Star of silver sweep across the skies,
show where Jesus in the manger lies;
shepherds swiftly from your stupor rise
to see the saviour of the world:
O now carry . . .

3 Angels, sing again the song you sang,
bring God's glory to the heart of man;
sing that Bethl'em's little baby can
be salvation to the soul:
O now carry . . .

4 Mine are riches — from your poverty,
from your innocence, eternity;
mine, forgiveness by your death for me,
child of sorrow for my joy:
O now carry . . .

104

SING ALLELUIA

Linda Stassen
Arr. Norman Warren

Cm Gm Cm Gm
Girls: Lord 1. Sing al - le - lu - ia to the
Men: 1. Sing al - le - lu - ia to the Lord
Cm E♭ G
Lord Sing al - le - lu - ia,
Je - sus is ri - sen
Je - sus is Lord
Sing al - le - lu - ia to the Lord
Cm Gm A♭ E♭
Al - le - lu - ia
Sing al - le - lu - ia Sing al - le - lu - ia

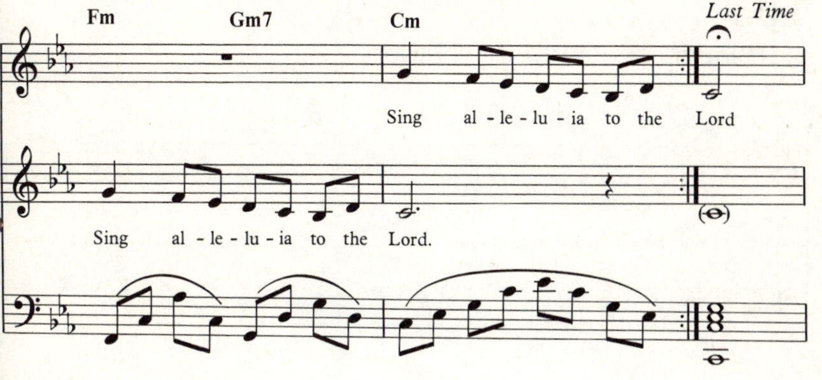
Fm
Gm7
Cm
Last Time
Sing al - le - lu - ia to the Lord
Sing al - le - lu - ia to the Lord.

2 Jesus is risen from the dead,
Jesus is risen from the dead;
Jesus is risen, Jesus is risen,
Jesus is risen from the dead.

3 Jesus is Lord of heaven and earth,
Jesus is Lord of heaven and earth;
Jesus is Lord, Jesus is Lord,
Jesus is Lord of heaven and earth.

4 Jesus is living in his church,
Jesus is living in his church;
Jesus is living, Jesus is living,
Jesus is living in his church.

5 Jesus is coming for his own,
Jesus is coming for his own;
Jesus is coming, Jesus is coming,
Jesus is coming for his own.

105

SOMEBODY'S KNOCKING AT YOUR DOOR

Unknown
Arr. Norman Warren

D G D G D G
Some-bo - dy's knocking at your door Some-bo - dy's knocking at your
D A7 D D7 G7 E7 D
door O sin-ner why don't you an-swer? Somebo - dy's
A7 D G D G6
knocking at your door. 1. Knocks like Je - sus Some-bo - dy's knock-ing at your
D F♯m A7 D G A D A7
door Knocks like Je - sus Somebo - dy's knocking at your door

D7
G7
E7
D
A7
D
O sin-ner why don't you an-swer? Somebo-dy's knocking at your door.

2 Can't you hear him? —
somebody's knocking at your door.
Can't you hear him? —
somebody's knocking at your door;
O sinner why don't you answer?
somebody's knocking at your door:
Somebody's knocking . . .

3 Answer Jesus! —
somebody's knocking at your door.
Answer Jesus! —
somebody's knocking at your door;
O sinner why don't you answer?
Somebody's knocking at your door.

106

SOVEREIGN LORD

Peter Jackson
Arr. Norman Warren

Slowly
D G6 A D G D Em A7 D A7 D
Sovereign Lord, so-vereign Lord, you made all things by your word; my cre-
G A7 F♯m Bm Bm7 G6 A7 D G D
- a-tor, re-deemer, my King of kings adored, sovereign Lord, sovereign Lord.

107

THE FULLNESS OF THE GODHEAD

Unknown
Arr. Norman Warren

D A7 D A

1. The full-ness of the God-head bo-di-ly dwells in my Lord. The

Em A7 D

full-ness of the God-head bo-di-ly dwells in my Lord. The full-ness of the

G D G D A7 D A7
Godhead bodily dwells in my Lord. And we are com-plete in him. Com-
D A7 D G D D G D A
-plete, com-plete, com-plete in him. We are com-plete in him. Al-le-lu-ia we're com-
D G D G D A7 D G D
-plete, com-plete, com-plete in him. We are com-plete in him.

2 It's not by works of righteousness
 but by his grace alone;
it's not by works of righteousness
 but by his grace alone;
it's not by works of righteousness
 but by his grace alone
that we are complete in him:
 Complete, complete . . .

3 There's nothing more that I can do —
 for Jesus did it all;
there's nothing more that I can do —
 for Jesus did it all;
there's nothing more that I can do —
 for Jesus did it all,
and we are complete in him:
 Complete, complete . . .

108

THE WELL IS DEEP

Words: adapted by Albert Orsborn
Music: Harry Woods
Arr. Norman Warren

E
E7
A
Am
E
B
The well is deep and I re-quire a drink of the wa-ter of
But none can quench my soul's de-sire for a
1
2
E
E
A
E
E
life.
life.
Till one draws near who the cry will heed
C♯m
A
F♯
B7
E
E7
Help-er of men in their time of need And I be-liev-ing
A
Am
E
B
B7
E
find in-deed that Christ is the wa-ter of life.

109

THERE'S NO GREATER NAME

Words and Music: M. A. Baughen

G Em Am D G Em Am D G B7
1. There's no grea-ter name than Je - sus, Name of him who came to save us In that
3. In our minds by faith pro - fess - ing, In our hearts by in-ward bless-ing, On our
Em G7 C Am6 Am G D7 1 G 2 D7 G Fine
sa-ving name of Je-sus eve-ry knee should bow. Christ is Lord.
tongues by words con-fess-ing, Je - sus
G D G Am E7 Am E Am D
2. Let ev-ery-thing that is 'neath the ground, Let eve-ry-thing in the world a-round,
G C A D D7
Let eve-ry thing that's high o'er the sky Bow at Je - sus' Name.

Da Capo al Fine (& 2nd Time bar)

110

WE SHALL SEE THE LORD IN GLORY

Words: Timothy Dudley-Smith
Arr. Norman Warren

G
C G D7
1. We shall see the Lord in glo – ry when he comes We shall
G
Am D
see the Lord in glo – ry when he comes As I
G G7 C Am
read the Gos – pel sto – ry We shall see the Lord in glo – ry, we shall
G Em Am D7 G
see the Lord in glo – ry when he comes.

Da Capo for Refrain

With the alleluias ringing to the sky,
with the alleluias ringing to the sky;
as I read the gospel story
we shall see the Lord in glory,
with the alleluias ringing to the sky!

2 We shall hear the trumpet sounded when he comes,
we shall hear the trumpet sounded when he comes;
we shall hear the trumpet sounded,
see the Lord by saints surrounded,
we shall hear the trumpet sounded when he comes!
With the alleluias ringing to the sky,
with the alleluias ringing to the sky;
we shall hear the trumpet sounded,
see the Lord by saints surrounded,
with the alleluias ringing to the sky!

3 We shall all rise up to meet him when he comes,
we shall all rise up to meet him when he comes,
when he calls his own to greet him,
we shall all rise up to meet him,
we shall all rise up to meet him when he comes!
With the alleluias ringing to the sky,
with the alleluias ringing to the sky;
when he calls his own to greet him,
we shall all rise up to meet him,
with the alleluias ringing to the sky!

111

WHAT A WONDERFUL SAVIOUR IS JESUS

Unknown
Arr. Norman Warren

A7
D
D7
G
A7
D
Bm
E7
A7
D
D7
G
D
A7
D
G
D
Chorus
D
D7
G
E7
A7
D
G
A7 (sus4)
A7
D
D7
G
E7
A7
D
G
D

Version 1

1 What a wonderful saviour is Jesus!
what a wonderful friend is he;
for he left all the glory of heaven,
came to earth to die on Calvary:
Sing hosanna, sing hosanna
sing hosanna to the King of Kings!
Sing hosanna, sing hosanna,
sing hosanna to the King!

2 He arose from the grave — alleluia!
and he lives never more to die;
at the Father's right hand interceding,
he will hear and heed our faintest cry:
Sing hosanna . . !

3 He is coming some day to receive us —
we'll be caught up to heaven above;
what a joy it will be to behold him —
sing forever of his grace and love!
Sing hosanna . . !

Version 2

1 Give me joy in my heart, keep me praising!
give me joy in my heart, I pray;
give me joy in my heart, keep me praising,
keep me praising till the break of day:
Sing hosanna, sing hosanna
sing hosanna to the King of Kings!
Sing hosanna, sing hosanna,
sing hosanna to the King!

2 Give me peace in my heart, keep me trusting . . .
Sing hosanna . . !

3 Give me love in my heart, keep me serving . . .
Sing hosanna . . !

112

WHAT GRACE

Unknown
Arr. David Peacock

(Capo 1)

E A E F♯m B7 F♯m B7 E B A E E7 A E F♯m B7 E7 A E F♯m B7 E

(Men) (Ladies) (Men) (Ladies) (Men) (Ladies) (All)

1. What grace! ___ God gave us his Son, what grace, ___ God gave us his Son, ___ what grace ___ God gave us his Son, what grace, what grace, God gave us his Son, what grace, what grace God gave us his Son.

V.S.

2 What *grace! — he died on the Cross . . .

3 What *grace! — he rose from the grave . . .

4 What *grace! — he's coming again . . .

5 What *grace! — alleluia! . . .

*or 'love'.

113

WHEN I SURVEY

Words: Isaac Watts
Music: Trad. Arr. D. G. Wilson

Without Piano
G D7 G Am7 Bm7 Em G6
G G C G
1. When I sur - vey the won-drous cross on which the
C Bm7 Am7 D7 G Am7
G D7 G
prince of glo - ry died, my rich-est gain I count but
Bm7 C G D7 G Am7 D7 G (C G)
G C D7 G C G
loss, and pour con - tempt on all my pride.

2 Forbid it, Lord, that I should boast
save in the cross of Christ my God;
the very things that charm me most—
I sacrifice them to his blood.

3 See from his head, his hands, his feet,
sorrow and love flow mingled down;
when did such love and sorrow meet,
or thorns compose so rich a crown?

4 Were the whole realm of nature mine,
that were an offering far too small;
love so amazing, so divine,
demands my soul, my life, my all.

114

WHO DOES JESUS LOVE?

Robert Stoodley

INTRO ‖: C F | C G :‖
(Short and lively!)
C F C G
1. Who does Je – sus love__ Je – sus love__
mf 2. Who does Je – sus care __ for Je – sus care__ for
3. Who did Je – sus come to serve__ come to serve__
4. What did Je – sus say __ Je – sus say__
p 5. Who did Je – sus die __ for Je – sus die__ for
(unaccompanied)
C C F C
Je – sus love?__ Who does Je – sus love?__
Je – sus care __ for? Who does Je – sus care __ for?
come to serve?__ Who did Je – sus come to serve?__
Je – sus say?__ What did Je – sus say?__
Je – sus die __ for? Who did Je – sus die __ for?
G [v3] C F C G
cresc.
Refrain
C F
He loves ev – er – y – one!
He cares for ev – er – y – one.
He came to serve ev – 'ry – one.
He said love ev – er – y – one.
He died for ev – er – y – one.
Well,
(tutti)
f Ev – 'ry –
cresc.

THE LORD JESUS CHRIST

C G C
should love___ Je – sus should love___ Je – sus
should care for Je – sus should care for Je – sus
– bo – dy should serve___ Je – sus should serve___ Je – sus
should love each oth – er should love each oth – er
should live for Je – sus should live for Je – sus
Fine
C F C G C (F C G)
should love___ Je – sus too!
should care for Je – sus too!
Ev – 'ry – bo – dy should serve___ Je – sus too!
should love each oth – er too!
should live for Je – sus too!

115

WHO IS JESUS?

Words: Jean Watson
Music: Norman Warren

D G D G F♯m
Who is Je - sus? Who is Je - sus? Who is
Bm Em A7 D G D
Je - sus? Would you like to know? 1. He's God's Son from hea - ven,
G D G D A7
that's who Je - sus is; he's God's Son from hea - ven, that's who Je-sus
D G D G D G
is; Who is Je - sus? Who is Je - sus?

F♯m Bm D A7 D
Who is Je – sus? Would you like to know?

2 He's our Lord and saviour . . .
Who is Jesus . . ?

3 He's the king of glory . . .
Who is Jesus . . ?

4 He's our loving shepherd . . .
Who is Jesus . . ?

5 He's the judge of all men . . .
Who is Jesus . . ?

116

WITH HEALING IN HIS WINGS

Unknown
Arr. Norman Warren

Gently

D G D Bm F♯m A7 D

1. With heal-ing in his wings, with heal-ing in his wings, the

D7 G A7 D G D A A7 G D

sun of right-eous-ness shall rise, with heal-ing in his wings.

2 Lord Jesus, now heal me,
Lord Jesus, now heal me!
The sun of righteousness shall rise—
Lord Jesus, now heal me!

117

WITH MY HEART I WORSHIP YOU

Norman Warren

Gently
D G D Bm
With my heart I wor - ship you — Je - sus,
Em Bm F♯m Bm E A F♯m
Je - sus; With my heart I wor-ship you — Je - sus,
D A D G D Bm
Je - sus: you gave all in love for me, saved me for e -
Em A Bm F♯m Gmaj7 Em6 D
- ter - ni - ty; with my heart I wor - ship you!

Alternative verses: With my lips I praise you . . .
With my life I serve you . . .

118

WITHOUT ME

Norman Warren

Brightly
Introduction
C Em Am Dm7 G11 C Cmaj7
f
With-out me ___ you can do
Am Dm G7 Em
no-thing, with-out me ___ there is no lov-ing, with-out me ___ there is no
Am C7 F Fmaj7 Dm E Am E
grow-ing, with-out me ___ there is no know-ing the Fa-ther's gift of
F G C F C
love; the Fa-ther's gift of love. ___

Repeat ad lib. Possible change in words of last line. The Fathers gift of *life . . . joy . . . peace . . .*

119

WONDERFUL AND MARVELLOUS

Unknown
Arr. Norman Warren

F Bb C7 F F7

1. Won-der-ful and mar-vel-lous is Je - sus to me, Sweet-er than the

Bb Gm C C7 F Am Am7 Dm Gm

hon-ey in the hon-ey-comb is he. Je - sus is real, he'll ne-ver

C7 Dm Gm C7 F

fail, I will serve him now and through-out all e - ter - ni - ty.

2 He is always with me as I'm walking along
I can hear a melody — he's given me a song:
Jesus is real, he'll never fail,
I will serve him now and throughout all eternity.

120

YOU ARE THE KING OF GLORY

Mavis Ford
Arr. Norman Warren

With majesty
F C7 F Bb Gm C
You are the king of glo - ry, you are the prince of peace,—

THE LORD JESUS CHRIST

A7 Dm Gm7 C
you are the Lord of heaven and earth, you're the sun of right-eous - ness!
A7 Dm Gm C Gm
An - gels bow down be - fore — you, wor - ship and a - dore, For
Am B♭ C Dm F C7 F
you have the words of e - ter-nal life, you are Je-sus Christ the Lord! — Ho-
B♭m Dm Gm Csus4 C
- san-na to the Son of Da - vid, ho - san-na to the King of — kings!
F C7 F Dm B♭ F C7 F
Glo - ry in the high - est hea - ven for Je - sus the mes - si - ah reigns!

121

YOU ARE WORTHY

Music: Pauline Michael Mills
Words: Pauline Michael Mills & Tom Smail
Arr. Norman Warren

Bb
Eb
Bb
F
1. You are wor-thy, you are wor-thy, you are wor-thy, O Lord;
Bb
Eb
Bb
you are wor-thy to re-ceive glo-ry, glo-ry and
Eb
Bb
F
Bb
hon-our and power: for you have cre-a-ted, have all things cre-
F
F7
Bb
-a-ted, for you have cre-a-ted all things; and for your

B♭7
E♭
C7
B♭
F7
B♭
plea-sure they are cre - a - ted; you are wor-thy, O Lord!

2 You are worthy, you are worthy,
you are worthy, O Lamb;
you are worthy to receive glory,
and power at the Father's right hand:
for you have redeemed us,
have ransomed and cleaned us
by your blood making us new;
in white robes arrayed us,
kings and priests made us,
and we are reigning in you.

122

ALL OVER THE WORLD

Unknown

C G7 C Dm G7
1. All ov-er the world the Spi-rit is mov-ing, all ov-er the
Dm G C C G7
world as the proph-et said it would be; all ov-er the
C E F F♯dim7
world there's a migh-ty rev-el-a-tion of the glo-ry of the
C Gm A7 Dsus4 Dm G7 C
Lord, as the wa-ters cov-er the sea.

2 Deep down in my heart the Spirit is moving,
deep down in my heart as the prophet said it would be;
deep down in my heart there's a mighty revelation
of the glory of the Lord, as the waters cover the sea.

123

KEPT BY THE POWER OF GOD

W. J. Graham Hobson

D A7 D A Bm A E7 A
Kept by the power of God, Kept by the power of God;

G A7 D Em7 F♯ Bm Em D A7 D
day by day, come what may, kept by the power of God.

Alternative verses: Kept by the love of God . . .
Kept by the grace of God . . .
Kept by the Spirit of God . . .

124

DO NOT STRIVE

Graham Kendrick
Arr. David Peacock

D
Em A7 D
G6 A7
1. Let me have my way a - mong you, do not strive, do not
1
2
D Fine D7
G A A7
strive; strive: For mine is the power and the
D A7 Bm D G Dm E7 A7
D.C. al Fine
glo - ry, for - e - ver and e - ver the same.

2 We'll let you have your way among us,
we'll not strive, we'll not strive. *Repeat*
For yours is the power and the glory
for ever and ever the same.
We'll let you have your way among us,
we'll not strive, we'll not strive.

3 Let my peace rule within your hearts,
do not strive, do not strive. *Repeat*
For mine is the power and the glory
for ever and ever the same.
Let my peace rule within your hearts,
do not strive, do not strive.

4 We'll let your peace rule within our hearts,
we'll not strive, we'll not strive. *Repeat*
For yours . . . *etc.*

125

O HOLY SPIRIT BREATHE ON ME

Norman Warren

F Am Gm C7 F Am
1. O Ho-ly Spi - rit breathe on me, O Ho-ly Spi - rit
Ped. Ped. Ped. Ped. Ped. Ped.
G7 C7 Am Dm7 Gm C7
breathe on me, and cleanse a-way my sin, fill me with love with-in:
Ped. Ped. Ped. Ped. Ped.
Last verse
F Gm7 C7 F Gm Am Gm F
O Ho-ly Spi - rit breathe on me.
Ped. Ped.

2 O Holy Spirit fill my life,
O Holy Spirit fill my life,
take all my pride from me,
give me humility:
O Holy Spirit breathe on me!

3 O Holy Spirit make me new,
O Holy Spirit make me new,
make Jesus real to me,
give me his purity:
O Holy Spirit breathe on me!

4 O Holy Spirit wind of God,
O Holy Spirit wind of God,
give me your power today,
to live for you always:
O Holy Spirit breathe on me!

126

RUACH, RUACH

Traditional. Arr. David Peacock

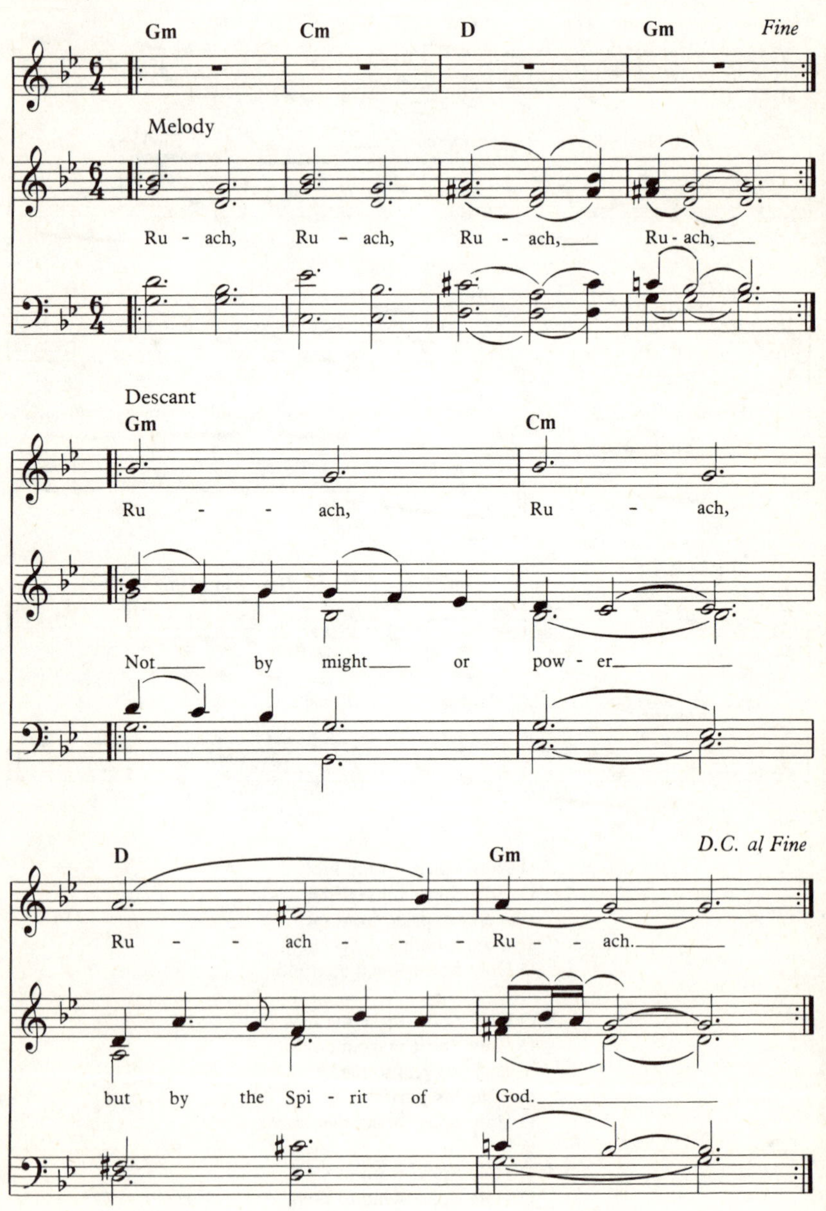
Gm
Cm
D
Gm
Fine
Melody
Ru - ach, Ru - ach, Ru - ach, Ru-ach,
Descant
Gm
Cm
Ru - - ach, Ru - ach,
Not by might or pow - er
D
Gm
D.C. al Fine
Ru - - ach - - - Ru - - ach.
but by the Spi - rit of God.

Ruach is the Hebrew word for 'Spirit', 'wind', or 'breath'.

127

SPIRIT OF GOD

Words: M. V. Old
Music: Traditional
Arr. Norman Warren

Chorus

G Am7 D7 G C G C

Spi - rit of God, un - seen as the wind, gen - tle as is the dove:

G Am7 D7 G C G *Fine*

teach us the truth and help us be - lieve, show us the saviour's love!

Em Am Em B7 Em

1. You spoke to men long, long a - go, gave us the writ - ten word;
2. With out your help we fail our Lord, we can not live his way;

D.C.
Em Am Em B7 Em D7
we read it still, need-ing its truth through it God's voice is heard.
we need your power, we need your strength, fol - low-ing Christ each day.

128

SPIRIT OF THE LIVING GOD

Daniel Iverson

First arrangement

F Gm D7 Gm F C7 F
1. Spi - rit of the liv - ing God, fall a-fresh on me,
C7 F B♭ Gm F C7 F
Spi - rit of the liv - ing God, fall a-fresh on me:
B♭ F G7 C C7
Break me, melt me, mould me, fill me—
F C F B♭ F C7 F
Spi - rit of the liv - ing God, fall a-fresh on me.

Second arrangement
Capo I

Daniel Iverson
Arr. David Peacock

E E7 F♯m C♯7 F♯m E F♯m B7
1. Spi - rit of the liv - ing God, fall a-fresh on
E B7 E B7 E A C♯7 F♯m E B7
me, Spi - rit of the liv - ing God, fall a-fresh on
E E7 A E F♯
me: break me, melt me, mould me,
B7 E E7 C♯7 F♯m F♯m E F♯m B7 E
fill me — Spi - rit of the liv-ing God, fall a-fresh on me.

2 Spirit of the living God, move among us all,
make us one in heart and mind, make us one in love:
humble, caring, selfless, sharing —
Spirit of the living God, fill our lives with love!

129

THANK YOU GOD FOR SENDING JESUS

Unknown
Arr. David Peacock

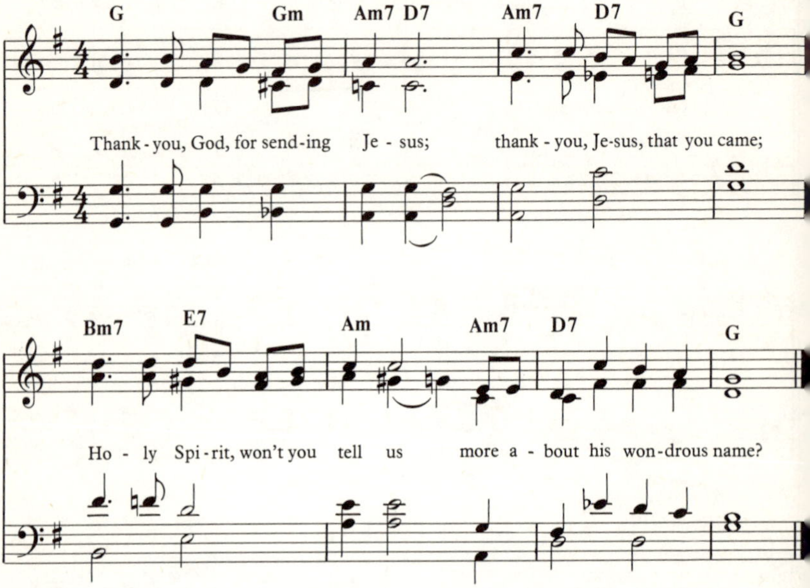

G Gm Am7 D7 Am7 D7 G

Thank-you, God, for send-ing Je - sus; thank - you, Je-sus, that you came;

Bm7 E7 Am Am7 D7 G

Ho - ly Spi-rit, won't you tell us more a - bout his won-drous name?

130

WHERE THE SPIRIT OF THE LORD IS

Graham Kendrick
Arr. Norman Warren

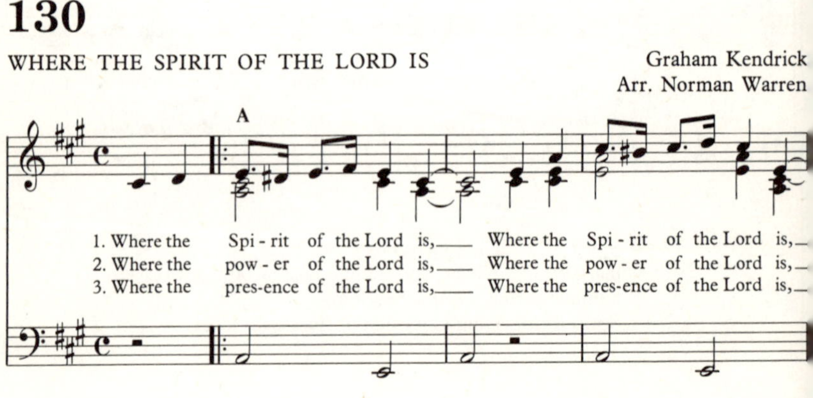
A
1. Where the Spi - rit of the Lord is, Where the Spi - rit of the Lord is,
2. Where the pow - er of the Lord is, Where the pow - er of the Lord is,
3. Where the pres-ence of the Lord is, Where the pres-ence of the Lord is,

v. 3
D
Dm A
there is li - ber-ty, there is li - ber-ty:
there is vic - to-ry, there is vic - to-ry,
there is full-ness of joy there is full-ness of joy
1
2
v. 3
E7
Where the and I will praise you O Lord, and I will
Where the and I will tri-umph O Lord, and I will
Where the and I will en-joy you O Lord, and I will en-
A
E7
praise you O Lord, And I will praise you O Lord
tri-umph O Lord, And I will tri-umph O Lord
-joy you O Lord, And I will en-joy you O Lord
1
2
(Clap) (Clap)
D A
(Clap) (Clap)
D A
Fine
in the Spi-rit. And I will Spi-rit.
2. Where the
3. Where the

131

WIND, WIND

Jane & Betsy Clowe
Arr. David Peacock

Chorus
D G A7 D F♯7 Bm Em
Wind, Wind blow on me; Wind, Wind set me free! Wind, Wind my Fa-ther sent the
A7 G D
bless-ed Ho-ly Spi-rit.
Verses
G A7
1. Je-sus told us all a-bout you, how we could not
D F♯7 Bm Em A7 Dsus4 D
live with-out you, with his blood the pow-er bought to help us live the life he taught.

2 When we're weary you console us,
when we're lonely you enfold us,
when in danger you uphold us,
blessed holy Spirit.
Wind, Wind . . .

3 When into the church you came,
it was not in your own but Jesus' name:
Jesus Christ is still the same—
he sends the Holy Spirit.
Wind, Wind . . .

4 Set us free to love our brothers,
set us free to live for others,
that the world the Son might see
and Jesus' name exalted be.
Wind, Wind . . .

132

A NEW COMMANDMENT

Unknown
Arr. Norman Warren

D Bm Em A F♯m
A new com-mand-ment that I give to you, is to love one an-
Bm G A D Bm G A7
-o-ther as I have loved you; is to love one an-o-ther as I have loved
D G F♯m Bm
you. By this shall all men know you are my dis-ci-ples: if
G G6 A6 3 D G A7
you have love one for an-o-ther; by this shall all men know
F♯m Bm D7 G A6 3 D
you are my dis-ci-ples: if you have love one for an-o-ther.

133

BIND US TOGETHER LORD

B. Gillman
Arr. Norman Warren

G
Bind us to-geth-er Lord, bind us to-geth-er with (O)
1
D
G
cords that can-not be bro-ken;
2
D
G
bind us to-geth-er in love!
G
D7
G
C6
D7
G
1. There is on-ly one God, there is on-ly one King,
C
G
C6
D7
G
D
there is on-ly one Bo-dy that is why we sing:

2 Made for the glory of God,
purchased by his precious Son,
born with the right to be clean,
for Jesus the victory has won:
Bind us together . . .

3 You are the family of God,
you are the promise divine,
you are God's chosen desire,
you are the glorious new wine:
Bind us together . . .

134

BROKEN FOR ME

Janet Lunt

Chorus
E
Amaj7
F♯m
B7
Bro-ken for me
(for me)
bro-ken for you;
the bo-dy of Je sus
bro ken for you;
Last time
F♯m B7
bro-ken for you.
Verses
v.1
1. He of-fered his bo-dy,
he poured out his soul,
Je-sus was bro-ken
that we might be whole:

2 Come to my table and with me dine,
eat of my bread and drink of my wine:
Broken for me . . .

3 This is my body given for you,
eat it remembering I died for you:
Broken for me . . .

4 This is my blood I shed for you,
for your forgiveness, making you new:
Broken for me . . .

135

CITY, O CITY

Lenny Smith
Arr. David Peacock

D F♯m G A D D7
1. Ci - ty, O ci - ty, O ci - ty of God
Em A7 Dsus2 D A7
glor - ious things are spo - ken of you;
1
2
A7 D G D G A7
spo - ken of you: Such glor - ious
3
D Em D7 G A7
things are spo - ken of

Dsus2 D Em A7 D F#m G A7
you, ci - ty, O ci - ty, O ci - ty of
D D7 Em A7 D G D
God; glor-ious things are spo - ken of you!

2 This one and that one were born in her—
all my springs of joy are in you;
this one and that one were born in her—
all my springs of joy are in you:
  Yes all my springs of joy are in you,
  this one and that one were born in her;
  all my springs of joy are in you!

3 Singers and dancers together say,
all my springs of joy are in you;
singers and dancers together say,
all my springs of joy are in you:
  Yes all my springs of joy are in you,
  singers and dancers together say,
  all my springs of joy are in you!

136

COME AND GO WITH ME

Unknown
Arr. David Peacock

First arrangement

E A E

1. Come and go with me to my Fa - ther's house,

B7 E B7 E

to my Fa-ther's house, to my Fa-ther's house; come and go with me

A E F♯m7 B7 E A E

to my Fa-ther's house where there's joy, joy, joy!

Second arrangement

Unknown
Arr. Norman Warren

G
C6
G
1. Come and go with me to my Fa - ther's house,

D
G
G
to my Fa-ther's house, to my Fa-ther's house; come and go with me

C6
G
C6
G
D7
G
to my Fa - ther's house where there's joy, joy, joy!

2 It's not very far to my Father's house,
to my Father's house, to my Father's house;
come and go with me to my Father's house
where there's joy, joy, joy!

3 There is room for all in my Father's house
in my Father's house, in my Father's house;
come and go with me to my Father's house
where there's joy, joy, joy!

4 Everything is free in my Father's house,
in my Father's house, in my Father's house;
come and go with me to my Father's house
where there's joy, joy, joy!

5 Jesus is the way to my Father's house
to my Father's house, to my Father's house;
come and go with me to my Father's house
where there's joy, joy, joy!

6 Jesus is the light in my Father's house,
in my Father's house, in my Father's house;
come and go with me to my Father's house
where there's joy, joy, joy!

137

THE GRACE

Music: Norman Warren

This may be sung with Solo or Group leading and the People repeating each phrase, or straight through by everyone without repeats.

Gm
Dm7
Gm
The grace of our Lord Je - sus Christ

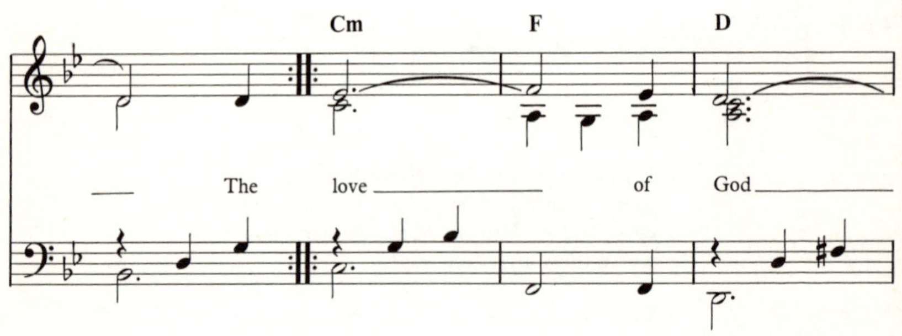
Cm
F
D
The love of God

D7
E♭
F
Gm
The fel - low - ship of the Ho - ly

1
C7
Gm
F
Gm
Spi - rit be with us all ev - er - more.
2
Cm
D
Gm
E♭
Tutti
Gm
The more, ev - er - more
Cm
G
A - men.

138

THE GRACE OF OUR LORD

Words and music: Steve Raven
Arr. Norman Warren

Gently
E B7 E E7
The Grace of our Lord Je - sus Christ, the
A Am E E7
Love of God, the
A B7 E B7 C♯m
fel - low - ship of the Ho - ly Spi - rit
F♯m B7 E
Last time to Coda
be with us all.
Verse
B7 E
1. We are your peo - ple in (Bri - tain), we
2. You give us our love for each other that

B7
E
E7
want you to work in our land: so
you might be seen where we live: so
A
Am
E
C♯7
take us and mould us and lead us but hold us and
help us to show it as oth - ers might know it — we
F♯7
F♯m7
B7
teach us to un - der - stand!
The
need you to help us to give.
CODA
F♯m
B7
E
For ev - er - more
F♯m
B7
E
A - - - - - men.

139

HE IS HERE, HE IS HERE

Jimmy Owens
Arr. David Peacock

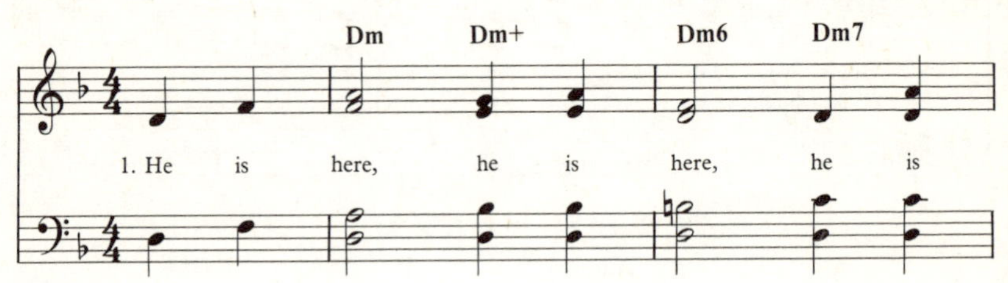
Dm
Dm+
Dm6
Dm7
1. He is here, he is here, he is

G
Gm
Dm
Dm7
mov - ing a - mong us; he is here, he is

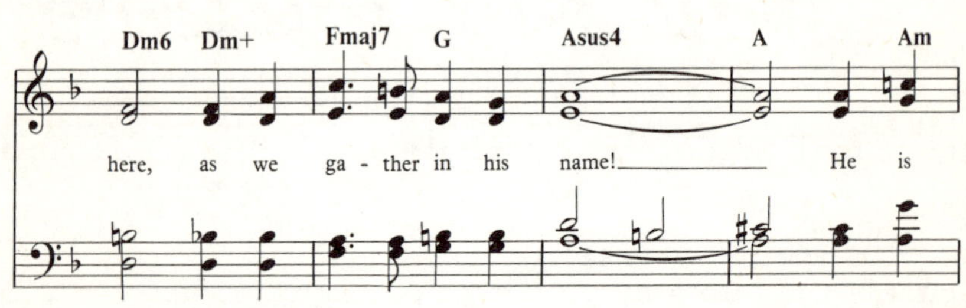
Dm6
Dm+
Fmaj7
G
Asus4
A
Am
here, as we ga - ther in his name! He is

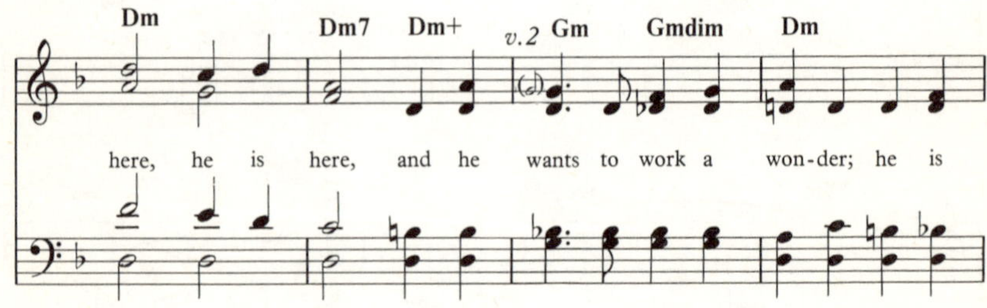
Dm
Dm7
Dm+
v.2
Gm
Gmdim
Dm
here, he is here, and he wants to work a won-der; he is

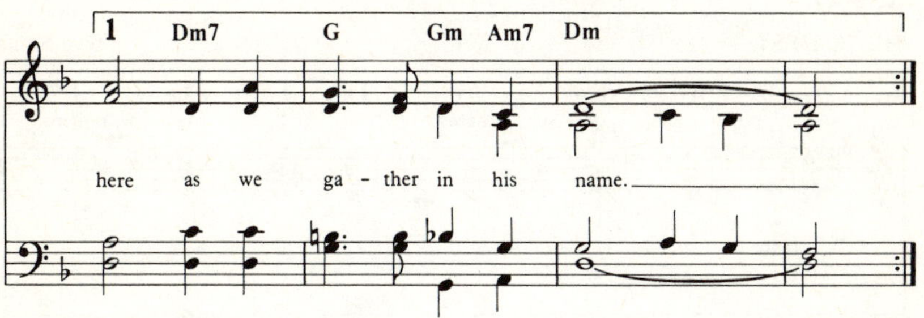
1
Dm7 G Gm Am7 Dm
here as we ga - ther in his name.

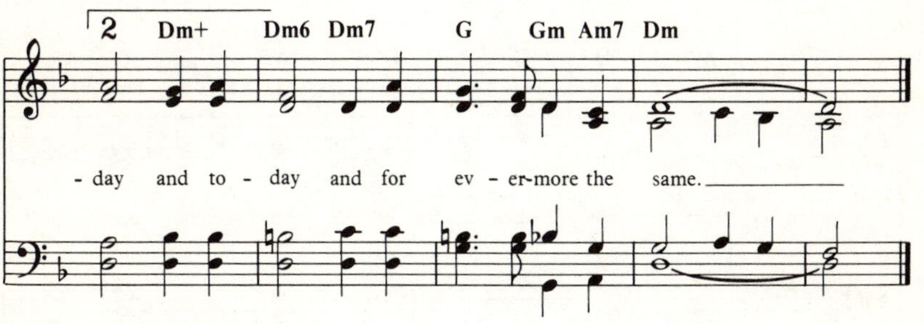
2
Dm+ Dm6 Dm7 G Gm Am7 Dm
- day and to - day and for ev - er-more the same.

2 He is Lord, he is Lord,
let us worship before him;
he is Lord, he is Lord,
as we gather in his name!
He is Lord, he is Lord,
let us praise and adore him—
yesterday and today
and for evermore the same.

140

HE IS HERE

Steve Stone

D B7 Em A7 Em E F♯m D7
Je - sus is here Je - sus is here
1. He is here he is here
G A7 D G D A7 D
Je - sus, Je - sus is here.
my heart tells me he is here.

2 He is Lord (Jesus is Lord!),
he is Lord (Jesus is Lord!):
*my heart tells me
he is Lord (Jesus, Jesus is Lord).

3 I will praise him (Jesus is Lord!),
I will praise him (Jesus is Lord!):
*my heart tells me
he is Lord (Jesus, Jesus is Lord!).

*or 'God's word tells me . . . '

141

JESUS STAND AMONG US

Graham Kendrick

F Gm C7 F
1. Je-sus stand a-mong us at the meet-ing of our lives. Be our sweet a-
2. So to you we're gath-ering out of each and ev-ery land, Christ the love be-
Gm C F B♭ Am
-gree-ment at the meet-ing of our eyes:
-tween us at the join-ing of our hands:
O Je-sus we love you,
B♭ Am B♭ F
so we ga-ther here join our hearts in u-ni-ty and
G7 1,2 C7 3 Gm C7 F
take a-way our fear. our fear.

Repeat verse 1

LET US BREAK BREAD TOGETHER

Words: (1) Trad, (2) J. E. Seddon
Calhoun Melody
Arr. Norman Warren

F Gm7 F B♭6 C7 F B♭ F Am Am7
1. Let us break bread to - ge - ther on our knees, let us break bread to -
Dm7 G7 C C7 F F7
- ge - ther on our knees: When I fall on my knees, with my
B♭ Gm F B♭ C7 F B♭ F
face to the ri - sing sun, O Lord, have mer - cy on me!

Version 1

2 Let us drink wine together on our knees,
let us drink wine together on our knees:
When I fall . . .

3 Let us praise God together on our knees,
let us praise God together on our knees:
When I fall . . .

Version 2

1 Let us praise God together,
let us praise;
Let us praise God together
all our days:
he is faithful in all his ways,
he is worthy of all our praise,
his name be exalted on high!

2 Let us seek God together,
let us pray;
let us seek his forgiveness
as we pray:
he will cleanse us from all sin,
he will help us the fight to win,
his name be exalted on high!

3 Let us serve God together,
him obey;
let our lives show his goodness
through each day:
Christ the Lord is the world's true light—
let us serve him with all our might,
his name be exalted on high!

143

PETER AND JOHN

Unknown
Arr. Norman Warren

G C D7
Pe - ter and John went to pray, They met a lame man on the
Sil - ver and gold have I none but such as I have I give
G v.2 C
way He asked for alms and held out his palms and
you In the name of Je - sus Christ of
D7 1 G 2 G
this is what Pe - ter did say.
Naz - a - reth rise up and walk.
He went walk-ing and leap-ing and
D D7 G C G
prais - ing God, Walk - ing and leap - ing and prais - ing God. 'In the
C Am D7 G
name of Je - sus Christ of Naz - a - reth rise up and walk.'

144

THERE'S A QUIET UNDERSTANDING

Tedd Smith
Arr. Norman Warren

Gently, with warmth
Am7 D7 G D C
Organ
1. There's a qui-et un-derstand ing
2. There's a love we feel in Je-sus,
Org. Em Bm Org. C
when we ga-ther in the Spirit,
Liv-ing bread he longs to feed us,
It's a pro-mise
D7 G Am7 D
that he gives us Org. when we ga-ther in his name.
Am7 D G A♭
when we ga-ther in his name.
3. And we know when

E♭ D♭ Org. Fm Cm
we're to - geth - er, shar - ing love and un - der - stand - ing,
Org. D♭ E♭7 A♭ B♭m7
that our bro - thers and our sis - ters Org. feel the oneness that he
E♭ A♭ E♭ D♭ Org. Fm
Org.
brings. 4. Thank you Je - sus, thank you Je - sus, for the way you
Cm Org. D♭ E♭7 A♭
love and feed us, for the ma - ny ways you lead us,
thank you Lord. Thank you Lord.

145

THIS IS THE DAY OF THE LORD

Charles High
Arr. Norman Warren

F Bb C7 F Gm F
This is the day of the Lord,

Bb Gm7 C F6 Bb Am
this is the day of the Lord, this is the day of the

Dm F Bb C7 F Bb F
Lord, Al - le - lu - ia, Al - le - lu - ia!

Alternative verses: This is the (feast. . . birthday. . . service. . . song) of the Lord.
We are the people of the Lord.
These are the praises of the Lord.

146

THIS IS THE DAY

Unknown
Arr. Norman Warren

E
B
1. This is the day, this is the day that the Lord has made, that the

Lord has made; we will re-joice, we will re-joice, and be
E B7 E E7
glad in it and be glad in it:
Chorus
A
This is the day that the
B B7 E A E B7 E
Lord has made we will re-joice and be glad in it;
E C♯m F♯m E B7 E
this is the day, this is the day that the Lord has made.

2 This is the day when he rose again . . .

3 This is the day when the Spirit came . . .

147

TO GOD'S LOVING KINDNESS

Michael Perry
Arr. Stephen Coates and Norman Warren

F
Gm
1. To God's lov - ing kind-ness we com - mit you, the
C7
F
A7
Lord bless your life and make you strong. May the praises of God, the
Dm
B♭
G7
C11
F
Fa - ther and the Son and the Spi - rit three in one be your song.

2 To God's holy favour we commend you,
the Lord hear your prayers and show his face.
And the mercy of God,
the Father and the Son
and the Spirit – Three in One,
bring you grace.

3 To God's great protection we entrust you,
the Lord take your hand and give you peace.
Let the blessing of God,
the Father and the Son
and the Spirit – Three in One,
never cease.

148

WE ARE ONE BODY

Words: Michael Perry
Music: Norman Warren

Gently
Em
A
Bm7
Em
Em7
1. We are one bo-dy in the Lord, we have
C
D7
G
E7
Am
D7
one Spi-rit and one call; there is one hope, one Lord,
Bm
E7
Am
Bm7
Em
A
Em
one faith, one life, one Fa-ther of us all!

2 There are some who can tend the flock,
there are some who can preach the word,
so that
some lead,
some serve,
some teach,
some build
one body in the Lord.

149

WE HAVE COME INTO HIS HOUSE

Bruce Ballinger
Arr. Norman Warren

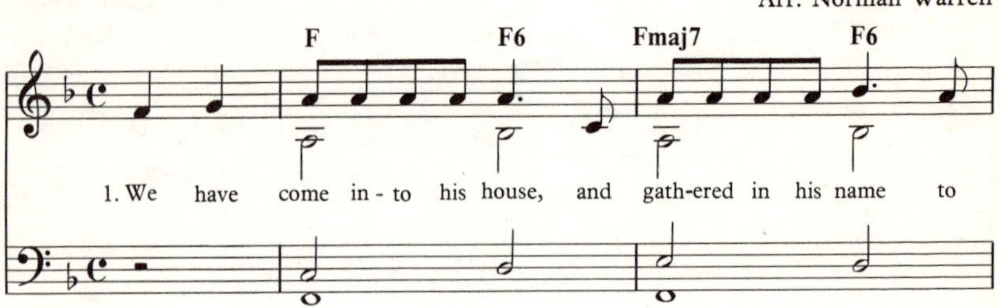
F F6 Fmaj7 F6
1. We have come in - to his house, and gath-ered in his name to

Gm7 C7 Gm Gm#7
wor - ship him; we have come in - to his house and

Gm7 C7 F
gath-ered in his name to wor - ship him; we have

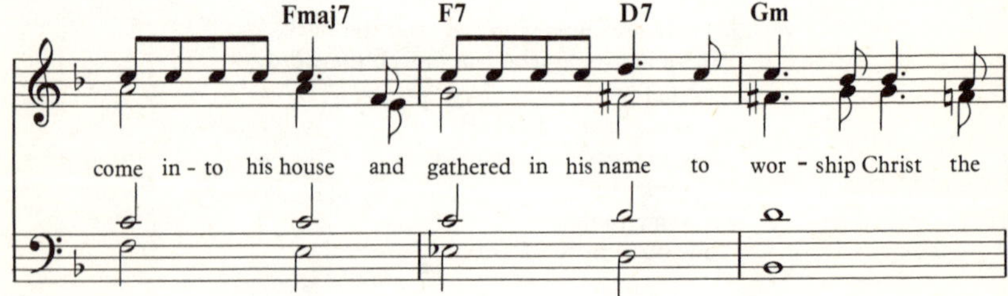
Fmaj7 F7 D7 Gm
come in - to his house and gathered in his name to wor - ship Christ the

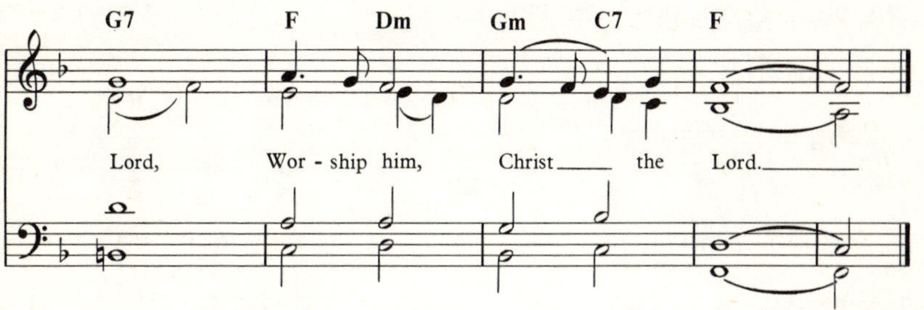
G7
F
Dm
Gm
C7
F
Lord,
Wor - ship him,
Christ
the
Lord.

2 Let's forget about ourselves
and concentrate on him and worship him;
let's forget about ourselves
and concentrate on him and worship him;
let's forget about ourselves
and concentrate on him and worship Christ the Lord,
worship him, Christ the Lord.

3 He is all our righteousness,
we stand complete in him and worship him;
he is all our righteousness,
we stand complete in him and worship him;
he is all our righteousness,
we stand complete in him and worship Christ the Lord,
worship him, Christ the Lord.

WE WILL COME INTO HIS PRESENCE

Norman Warren

Slowly
Em A Em Em7
We will come in - to his pre - sence with thanks -
C D Em Em7 Am D
giv - ing in our hearts, we will come in - to his
Am Am7 F G Am Am7
pre - sence with thanks - giv - ing in our hearts sing - ing:
Verse
Dm Am B7 Em B
1. Ho - ly, ho - ly is the Lord, ho - ly,

B7
Em
Am
Em
ho - ly is the Lord.

2 Worthy is the Lamb that died,
worthy is the Lamb that died!
We will come . . .

3 Glory to our risen king,
glory to our risen king!
We will come . . .

4 Jesus Christ is Lord of all,
Jesus Christ is Lord of all!
We will come . . .

5 Holy, holy is the Lord,
holy, holy is the Lord!
We will come . . .

151

ALL MY HEART

Unknown
Arr. Norman Warren

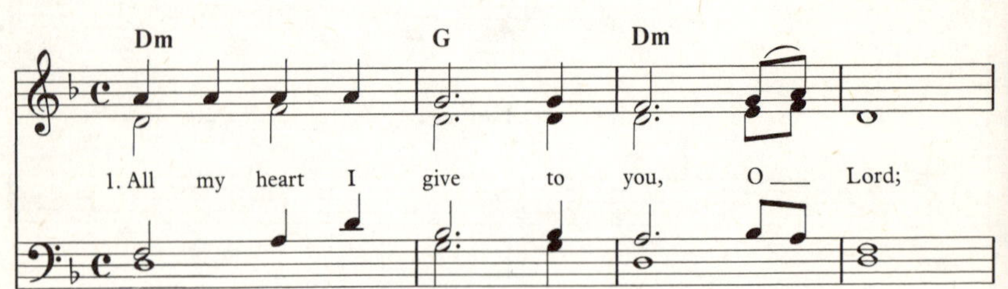
Dm
G
Dm
1. All my heart I give to you, O ___ Lord;

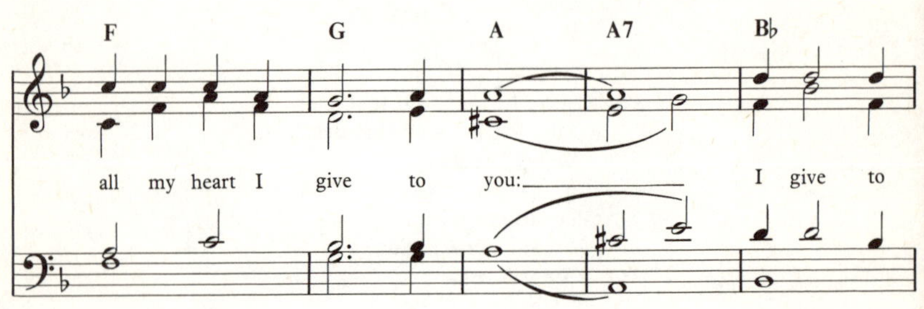
F
G
A
A7
B♭
all my heart I give to you: ___ I give to

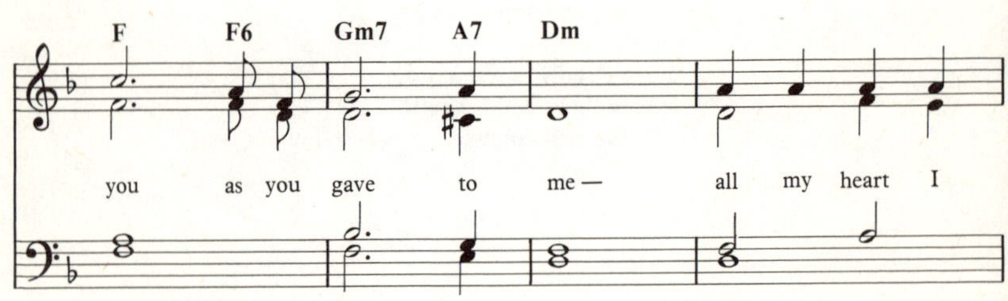
F
F6
Gm7
A7
Dm
you as you gave to me — all my heart I

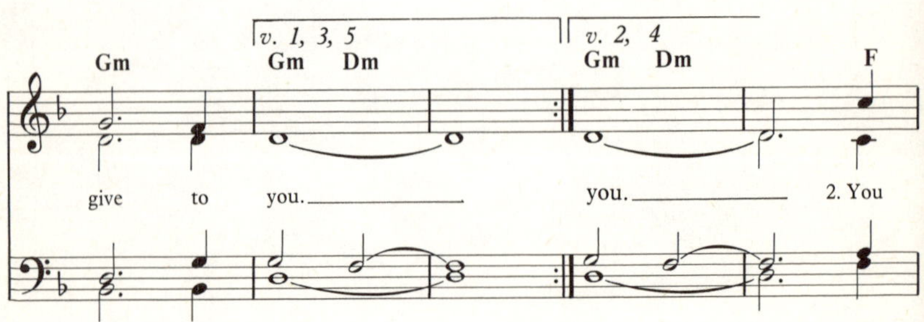
v. 1, 3, 5
v. 2, 4
Gm
Gm Dm
Gm Dm
F
give to you. ___ you. ___ 2. You

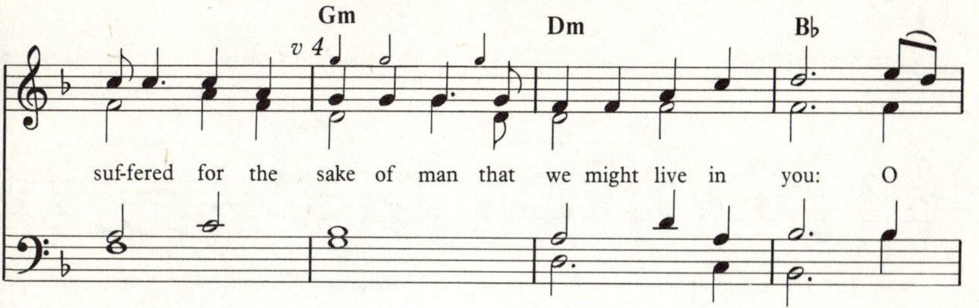
Gm
Dm
B♭
v 4
suf-fered for the sake of man that we might live in you: O

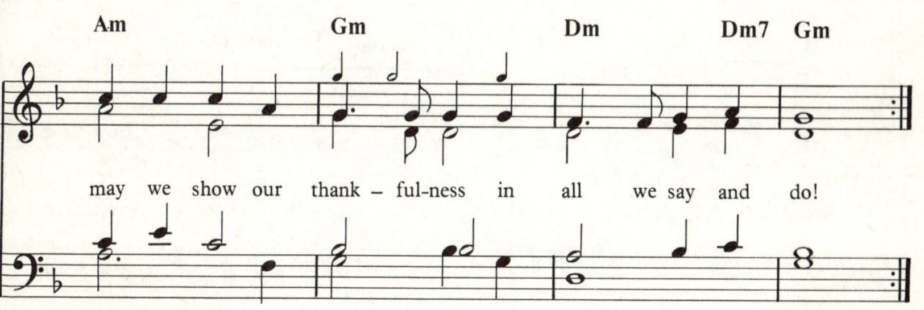
Am
Gm
Dm
Dm7
Gm
may we show our thank – ful-ness in all we say and do!

1 All my heart I give to you, O Lord;
all my heart I give to you:
I give to you as you gave to me —
all my heart I give to you.

2 You suffered for the sake of man
that we might live in you:
O may we show our thankfulness
in all we say and do!

3 All my life I give to you, O Lord;
all my life I give to you:
I give to you as you gave to me —
all my life I give to you.

4 Sing glory to the Father,
sing glory to the Son,
sing glory to the Spirit —
to God the Three-in-One.

5 All myself I give to you, O Lord;
all myself I give to you:
I give to you as you gave to me —
all myself I give to you.

152

ALL SCRIPTURES

Words and Music by M. A. Baughen
Arr. W. Wooldridge

C7 F Gm7 F B♭ B♭6 C7

1. All Scrip-tures are giv-en by the breath of God,_ are in-spired of God,_ are the

F C C7 F B♭m F F6 F+

word of the Lord; all Scrip-tures are giv - en by the breath of God,_ and

C7 F *Fine* C F

glor - i - fy his name! They can make you wise to a

C Am7 Fm C G C

sav - ing faith in Je - sus Christ_ the Lord; they can

C7 F E7 Am F C Cm F G7 C7 *D.C.*

make the man of God com-plete, and are meant to be his sword!

2 So study to show yourself approved to God,
fit to use his word,
fit to speak in his name;
so study to show yourself approved to God,
a workman not ashamed:
They'll reprove, correct, and a training in
all righteous living afford;
they will yield up all that we need to know
of the teaching of the Lord!

3 All Scriptures are given by the breath of God,
are inspired of God,
are the word of the Lord;
all Scriptures are given by the breath of God,
and glorify his name!

153

BE STILL AND KNOW

Unknown
Arr. D. Peacock

D G D A A7 D
1. Be still and know that I am God, be
G G7 E A F♯7
still and know that I am God, be
Bm A7 D G D A7 D
still and know that I am God.

2 I am the Lord who heals your pain . . .

3 In you, O Lord, I put my trust . . .

154

Words: M. A. Lathbury
Music: W. F. Sherwin

BREAK NOW THE BREAD OF LIFE

D G D A D

Break now the bread of life, dear Lord, to me, as you once

G A B7 A E7 A A7 G D

broke the loaves be – side the ___ sea: be – yond the sa – cred page

A E7 A A7 D Em7 A7 D

I seek you Lord — my spi-rit longs for you, O Liv – ing Word!

155

COME LORD JESUS

Norman Warren

Am
F
Dm7
1. Come Lord Je-sus, come Lord Je-sus, come and

G7 C E7 A A6
make our hearts your home! — we bow — be – fore you, we
D A F♯m F
love and a – dore you, ac – know – ledge that you are Lord of
E E7 Am F
all: — come Lord Je – sus, come Lord
Dm7 G7 C
D.C.
Fine
After v. 1, 2 only
Je – sus come and make our hearts your home. —

2 Come Lord Jesus, come Lord Jesus,
come and make our hearts your throne! —
we bow before you, we love and adore you,
acknowledge that you are Lord of all:
Come Lord Jesus, come Lord Jesus,
come and make our hearts your throne.

3 Come Lord Jesus, come Lord Jesus,
come and make this world your own! —
we bow before you, we love and adore you,
acknowledge that you are Lord of all:
Come Lord Jesus, come Lord Jesus,
come and make this world your own.

156

DAY BY DAY

Words: Richard of Chichester
Music: Norman Warren

D
G
D
G
Day by day, day by day,

D
Dmaj7
Bm
F♯m
Em
dear Lord, of you three things I pray:

A
Bm
F♯m
to see you more clear – ly, to

G
D
F♯
love you more dear – ly, to fol – low you more

PRAYER AND THE BIBLE

F♯ Bm Em7 A7 D A7 D D7
near – ly, day by day; to
B° E7 Amaj7 Bm G A
see you more clear – ly, to love you more
D G F♯ C7 B7 F♯
dear – ly, to fol – low you more near – ly,
D A7 D G D G D
day by day, day by day!

157

GIVE US PEACE — *A Round* (Dona Nobis Pacem)

Unknown

1
Do - na no - bis pa - cem, pa - cem;
Give us, Give us, give us your peace;
Dona no - bis pa - - cem!
Give give us give us your peace!
2
Do - na no - bis pa - cem;
Give us, give us your peace;
Do - na no - bis pa - - cem!
Give us, give us give us your peace!
3
Do - na no - bis pa - cem;
Give us, give us your peace;
Do - na no - bis pa - - cem!
Give us, give us give us your peace!

158

KUM BA YAH

Trad.
Arr. Norman Warren

D
G
D
1. Kum ba yah, my Lord, Kum ba yah, Kum ba

F♯m
A
D
D
G
yah, my Lord, Kum ba yah, Kum ba yah, my Lord, Kum ba

A7
D
A7
D
G6
A7
D
yah: O Lord, Kum ba yah!

2 Someone's crying Lord, kum ba yah . . !

3 Someone's singing Lord, kum ba yah . . !

4 Someone's praying Lord, kum ba yah . . !

159

LIGHTEN OUR DARKNESS

Chris Humphries

Evening collect *(Series 3)*

D
Em
B7
Em
Light - en our dark - ness,
Lord we pray
G
A
F♯m
Bm
and in your mer - cy,
and in your mer - cy de -
Em
A7
D
fend us from all pe - rils and
dan - gers of this night:
D
G
3
F♯m
Em
Light - en our dark - ness for the
love of your on - ly Son, our
G
A7
Bm
Em
A
sa - viour Je - sus
Christ.
A - -

D
D
1
2
- men.
- men.
Light - en our dark - ness

160

LORD, I WANT TO BE A CHRISTIAN

Trad.
Arr. Norman Warren

D G6 A7 D A7 D G

1. Lord, I want to be a Christ-ian in my heart, in my heart. Lord, I

D G6 A7 D G

want to be a Christ-ian in my heart, in my heart, in my

F♯m A7 D Dmaj7 Bm D G6 A7 D

heart; Lord, I want to be a Christ-ian in my heart!

2 Lord, I want to be more loving
in my heart . . .

3 Lord, I want to be more holy
in my heart . . .

4 Lord, I want to be like Jesus
in my heart . . .

161

MAKE ME A CHANNEL OF YOUR PEACE

Words: after St. Francis of Assisi
Music: S. Temple
Arr. Norman Warren

D
1. Make me a chan - nel of your peace Where
F♯m Em7 F♯m G6 v3 A7 Em
there is hat - red let me bring your love, where there is in - ju -
A7 G D A7
- ry your par - don Lord and where there's doubt true faith in
D D7 G D
Fine Chorus
you: O Mas - ter grant that I may ne - ver seek

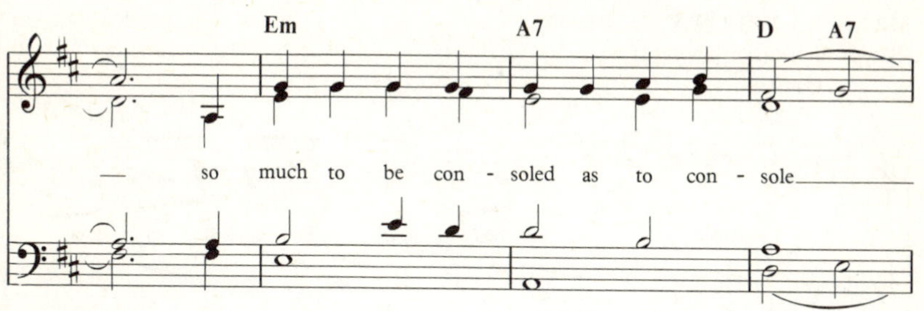
Em
A7
D
A7
— so much to be con - soled as to con - sole

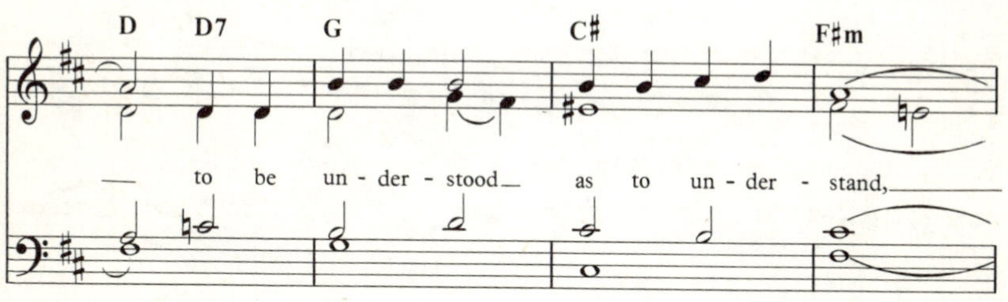
D
D7
G
C♯
F♯m
— to be un - der - stood as to un - der - stand,

Bm
E7
A
— to be loved as to love with all my soul.

2 Make me a channel of your peace:
where there's despair in life let me bring hope,
where there is darkness, only light,
and where there's sadness, ever joy:
O Master grant that I may never seek . . .

3 Make me a channel of your peace:
it is in pardoning that we are pardoned,
in giving of ourselves that we receive,
and in dying that we're born to eternal life.
O Master grant that I may never seek . . .

Repeat verse 1 without chorus.

MAKE US WORTHY, LORD
(Prayer of Mother Theresa)

Words: Mother Theresa
Music: Norman Warren

Gently
D F♯m G D
1. Make us ___ wor- thy, Lord, to serve our fel - low men
Em Bm C D
through-out the world who live in po - ver - ty and hun - ger, in
Am7 F♯m F D G
po-ver-ty and hun-ger, in po - ver - ty and hun - ger. ___
Ped.
D F♯m G D
2. Give them through our hands this day their dai - ly bread,
Em Bm C D
and by our un - der - stand - ing love, give peace and joy, give

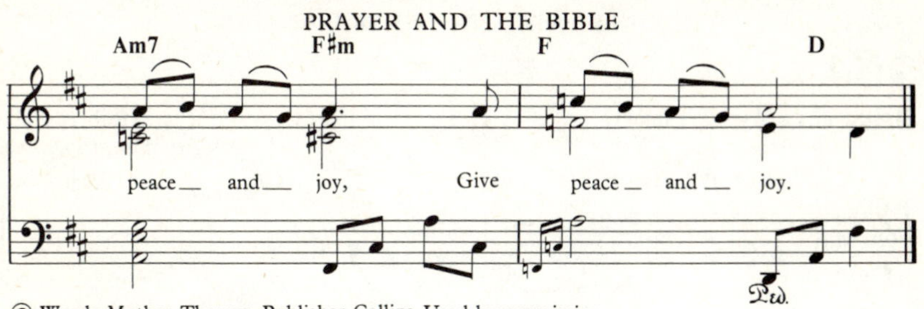

Am7 F♯m F D
peace_ and_ joy, Give peace_ and_ joy.

163

MAY THE GRACE

St. Aidan's Community
Arr. D. Peacock

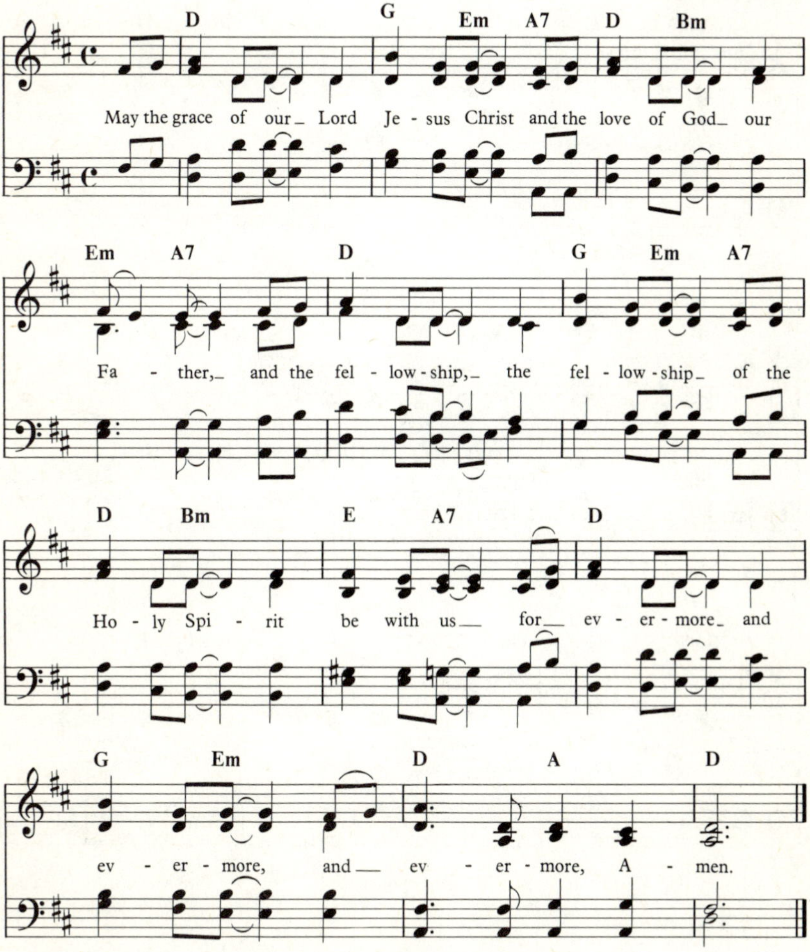

D G Em A7 D Bm
May the grace of our_ Lord Je - sus Christ and the love of God_ our
Em A7 D G Em A7
Fa - ther,_ and the fel - low - ship,_ the fel - low - ship_ of the
D Bm E A7 D
Ho - ly Spi - rit be with us_ for_ ev - er - more_ and
G Em D A D
ev - er - more, and_ ev - er - more, A - men.

164

OPEN OUR EYES, LORD

Robert Cull
Arr. David Peacock

D A7 D G A7 G6 D Bm
O-pen our eyes, Lord, we want to see Je - sus, to
Bm7 G G6 A7 G6 D
reach out and touch him and say that we love him;
B7 Em A7 G6 D Bm
o-pen our ears Lord, and help us to lis - ten: O
Bm7 G G6 A7 Dsus4 D
o-pen our eyes, Lord, we want to see Je - sus!

165

OUR FATHER IN HEAVEN

David Peacock

Not too slow
Soliste: C
G
Am7 G7
People: *
C
1. Our Fa - ther in hea - ven, Our Fa - ther in
2. Yours is the king - dom For yours is the
G
Am7 G7
Am
Em
Fmaj7
Em7
hea - ven, ho - ly is your name
king - dom and the power and glo - ry
Dm
Gsus4
G7
C
G
Am7
G
may your king-dom come O Lord
yours is the king-dom the pow'r and the glo - ry
Asus4
A7
D
A
Bm
A7
May your will be done here on earth
(v.2 For) ev - er and ev - er (For)

*People repeat each line after soloist

PRAYER AND THE BIBLE

Bm F♯m G F♯m Em Asus4
As it is in hea - ven Give us the food we need
A - men, A-men, A-men. For ever Lord

2nd time to Coda

A7 D A Bm7 A Fm7 B♭7

for to - day.

A - men. *(to Coda)*

Slower
more meditative

1 2

E♭maj7 D♭maj7 B♭7 D♭maj7 B♭7

Please for-give us the sins we have done sins we have done. As

1 2

A♭maj7 Gm7 Fm7 B♭7 F♯m7

we for - give As The

PRAYER AND THE BIBLE

Amaj7 G♯m7 F♯m7 B7 Amaj7 G♯m7 C7
People:
sins that o-thers have done__ to us, the sins that o-thers have done
__ to us
Fmaj7 E♭maj7 Cm7
Do not bring us to hard test - ing
First Tempo
D. 𝄋 al Coda or to *
Fmaj7 E♭maj7 Cm7 Gsus4 G
And pro-tect us from all ev - il Lord._ v. 2 For
CODA
Bm7 A7 D F G A
__ A - men,__ A - men.
3

1. 2nd verse may be sung, without repeats, by soloist and people together. In which case verse 2 begins at *.
2. The Coda may be sung by soloist or treated as an instrumental ending.

166

TURN YOUR EYES

Words and Music
H. H. Lemmel

F
C
C7
Dm
F7
Turn your eyes up - on Je - sus, look
B♭
G9
C
F
C7
full in his won - der - ful face; and the
F
C♯°
Dm
F7
B♭
Dm
Gm
things of earth will grow strange - ly dim in the
F
C
F
C7
F
light of his glo - ry and grace!

167

UNTO YOU, O LORD

Unknown
Arr. David Peacock

F
Descant (girls)
1. Un - to you O Lord,
Melody:
1. Un - to you O Lord,
F7
D7
Gm
do I lift up my
do I lift up my soul,
C7
soul,
un - to you O Lord,
un - to you O Lord,

F *Chorus* C7

— do I lift up my soul: —

do I lift up my soul, — O my

F F7 B♭

O my God, I trust in

God, — I trust in you, —

F Dm
you — let me not be a - shamed, let not my en - em - ies
— let me not be a - shamed, let not my en - em - ies

Gm7
C7
F
B♭
F
tri - umph ov - er me!
tri - umph ov - er me!

2 Show me your ways, (show me your ways,)
your ways O Lord, (your ways O Lord;)
teach me your paths, (teach me your paths,)
your paths O Lord, (your paths O Lord:)
O my God . . .

3 Remember not, (remember not)
the sins of my youth, (the sins of my youth;)
remember not, (remember not,)
the sins of my youth, (the sins of my youth:)
O my God . . .

4 The secret of the Lord, (the secret of the Lord)
is with them that love him, (with them that love him;)
the secret of the Lord, (the secret of the Lord)
is with them that love him, (is with them that love him;)
O my God . . .

168

YOU WILL KEEP HIM IN PERFECT PEACE

Norman Warren

2 part round

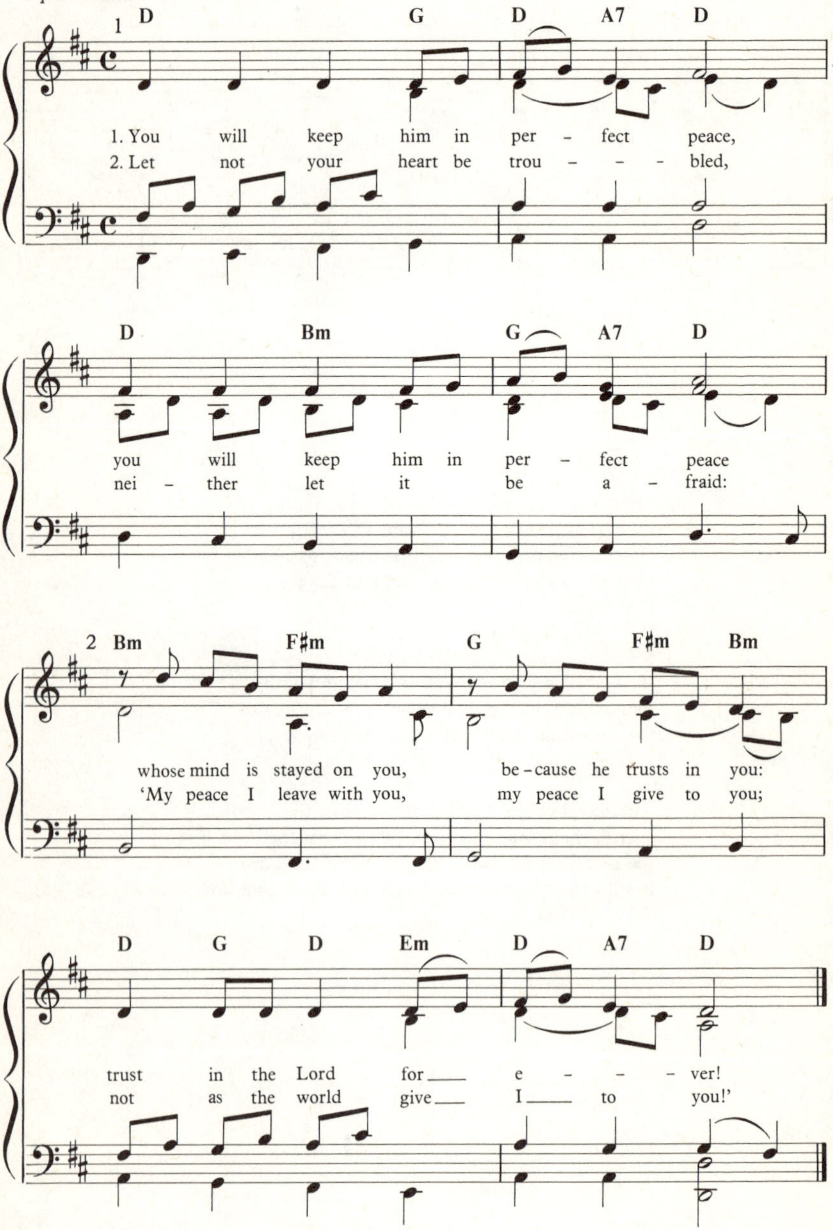

1. You will keep him in perfect peace, you will keep him in perfect peace whose mind is stayed on you, because he trusts in you: trust in the Lord for ever!

2. Let not your heart be troubled, neither let it be afraid: 'My peace I leave with you, my peace I give to you; not as the world give I to you!'

169

ALL THAT I AM, HE MADE ME

Words: Horace R. Jones
Music: Jack Ward

F Bb D7
All that I am, he made me,

Gm C F D7
all that I have he gave me; and all that ev - er I

Gm F C7 F
hope to be, Je - sus a - lone must do for me.

170

AND YOU SHALL SEEK ME

Jeremiah 29:13
Robert Rhodes

C A7 Dm G
And you shall seek me, and you shall
F C Am Dm
find me when you shall search for me
E7 Am C7
with all your heart; and I will be
3
3
A♭ C
found of you, and I will be found of you
3
3

Am A Dm G7
— when you shall seek me — with all your
C G7 C C7 A♭
heart. And I will be found of you, —
C Am A
— and I will be found of you, — when you shall
Dm G C F C
seek me — with all your heart. —

171

BRING FORTH THE FRUIT OF THE SPIRIT

Words: Michael Baughen
Music: David Peacock

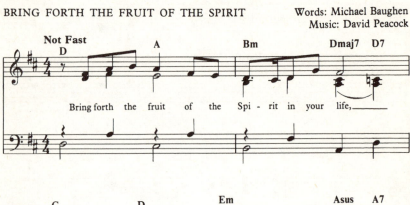

Not Fast

D A Bm Dmaj7 D7

Bring forth the fruit of the Spi - rit in your life,

G D Em Asus A7

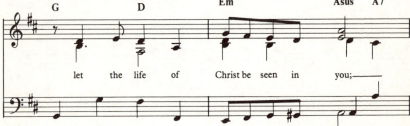

let the life of Christ be seen in you;

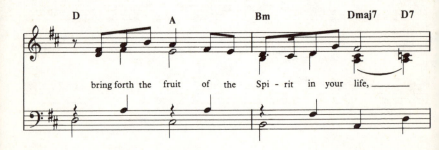

D A Bm Dmaj7 D7

bring forth the fruit of the Spi - rit in your life,

G F♯m Bm Em A7 D *Fine*
and let the Lord be glor - i - fied in you!

G G+ Em G7
Seek his pa - tience and his kind - ness,

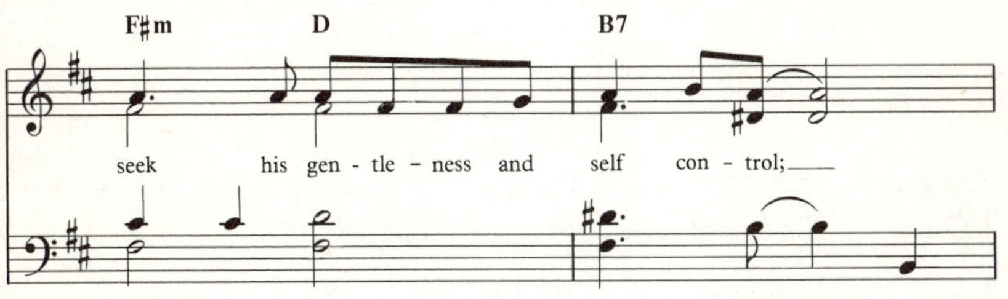
F♯m D B7
seek his gen - tle - ness and self con - trol;

Em C A7
seek his good - ness and his faith - ful - ness, and

D.C. al Fine
D B7 Em7 Asus A7
seek most his peace and joy and love.

172

BY FLOWING WATERS

Words and Music: Michael Perry
Arr. Christian Strover

Em
B7
1. By flow-ing wa-ters of Ba-by--lon
Em
B7
we hung our harps on the wil-lows;
Em
Am
C
how shall we sing our Je-hov-ah's song in a
Em
Bm7
Em
for-eign land, far a-way?

2 They who oppress us and mock our grief
tell us to sing and be merry;
how can we worship when spirits fail
in an alien land far away?

3 If we forget you, Jerusalem,
may we keep silence for ever! —
still we remember our distant home
in another land far away.

173

BY THE WATERS Unknown

3 part round

1
Bm
A
G
By the wa - ters, the wa - ters of
F♯
B
2
Ba - by - lon we lay down and wept and
wept for you Zi - on:
3
we re - mem - ber,
we re - mem - ber, we re - mem - ber you Zi - on.

174

CHRIST IN ME

Gary Garcia
Arr. David Peacock

Not too fast
C G Am F G7 C G7
Christ in me is to live to die is to gain,
C G Am F G G7 C C7
Christ in me is to live — to die is to gain, He's my
F G7 Em Am Dm7 G7 C C7
king, he's my song, he's my life and he's my joy; he's my
F G7 Em Am B♭ F C G7
strength, he's my sword, he's my peace and he's my Lord!
C G Am F G7 1 C G7 2 C
Christ in me is to live — to die is to gain! gain.

175

CLEANSE ME

Words and Music: R. Hudson Pope

G G° G D7 G D9 D7
Cleanse me from my sin, Lord, put your power with - in, Lord,
G G+ Am9 Am A A7 D7
take me as I am, Lord, and make me all your own:
G7 C E7 Am
keep me day by day, Lord, un - der - neath your sway, Lord;
G° F♯7 E♭7 G Em Am G D7 G
make my heart your pa - lace and your roy - al throne.

COME, GO WITH ME TO THAT LAND

Traditional
Arr. Norman Warren

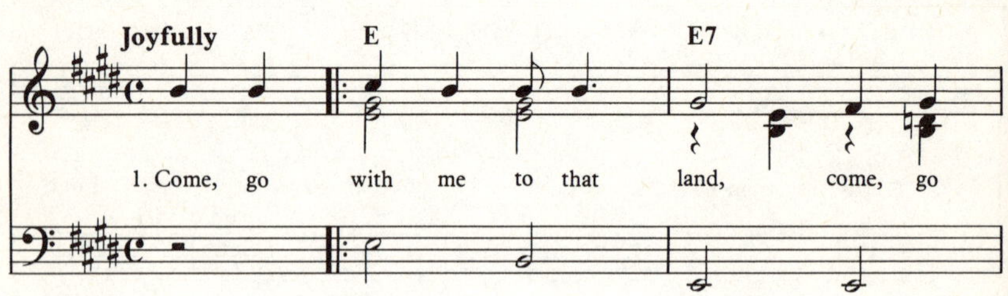
Joyfully
E
E7
1. Come, go with me to that land, come, go

A
E
with me to that land, come go with me to that

F♯m
B7
land where I'm bound: come, go

E
E7
A
with me to that land, come, go with me to that

C
E
A
land, to that land, to that

F♯m
B7
E
Fine
land, where I'm bound!

2. I'll see Jésus in that land

3. All God's people will be there

4. There'll be peace in that land

177

DO NOT BE WORRIED

G. Taylor

Unison
D
Em
A7
D
D7
1. Do not be wor-ried and up
go and pre-pare a place for

B7
Em
Em♯7
Em7
A7
set, be-lieve in God, be-lieve al-so in me:
you, I will come back and take you to my-self,

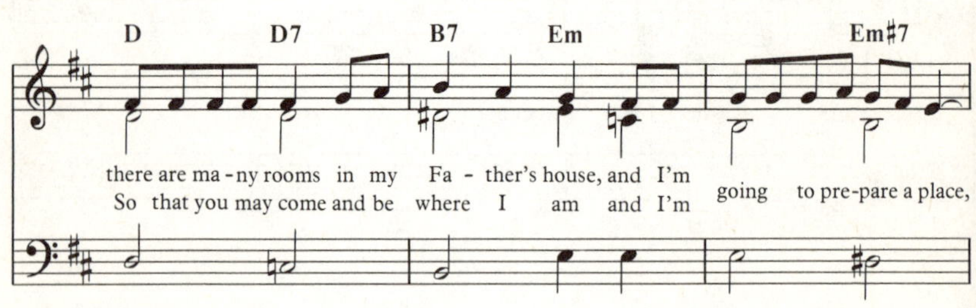
D
D7
B7
Em
Em♯7
there are ma-ny rooms in my Fa-ther's house, and I'm
So that you may come and be where I am and I'm
going to pre-pare a place,

Em7
A7
D
Em7
D
Chorus (4 part)
pre-pare a place for you.
I am the way,

G A7 F♯m Bm Em A7
the truth and the life; no one goes to the Fa-ther ex-
D G A7 F♯m Unison
cept by me I am the way, the truth and the life, and I'm
Em Em♯7 Em7 A7 1 D Em7
go-ing to pre-pare a place, pre-pare a place for you.
D 2 D Em Em♯7
2. Af-ter I you and I'm go-ing to pre-pare a place,
Em7 A7 D G D
pre-pare a place for you.

178

DO NOT JUDGE OTHERS
(Luke 6. 37-42; Matthew 7. 1-12)

C. R. Vaughan
Whitfield Jn. School, Liverpool 6

Capo on first fret

Lively ♩ = 116

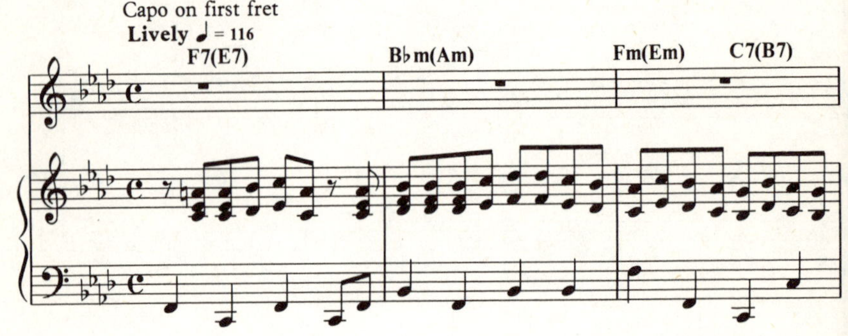
F7(E7)
B♭m(Am)
Fm(Em)
C7(B7)

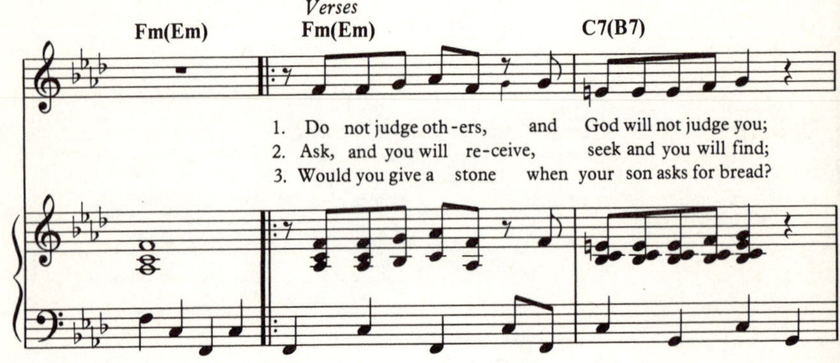
Fm(Em)
Verses
Fm(Em)
C7(B7)
1. Do not judge oth-ers, and God will not judge you;
2. Ask, and you will re-ceive, seek and you will find;
3. Would you give a stone when your son asks for bread?

Fm(Em)
Don't con-demn oth-ers, and God won't con-demn you;
Knock, and the door will be op-ened from be-hind.
Or give a snake when he asks for fish in-stead?

THE CHRISTIAN LIFE
F7(E7)
B♭m(Am)
For-give the oth-ers, and God will for-give you;
Do for the oth-ers what you want them to do;
Bad as you are, you know how to give the good;
Give to
Fm(Em)
C7(B7)
Fm(Em)
E♭7(D7)
oth-ers, and ___ God will give to you.
Chorus
A♭(G)
D♭(C)
E♭7(D7)
Speck, speck, speck in your broth-er's eye, ___ Log, log, log in your
A♭(G)
A♭(G)
own eye, eye, ___ eye, eye, eye; Take the log out of your

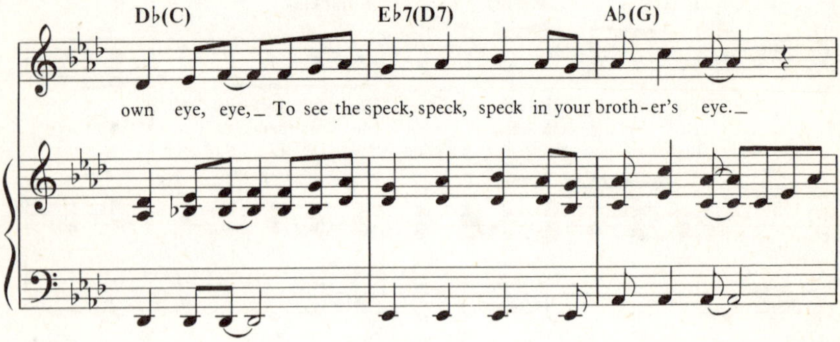

Db(C) Eb7(D7) Ab(G)

own eye, eye,_ To see the speck, speck, speck in your broth-er's eye._

1 2 | 3

Bbm7(Am7) C7(B7) Eb7(D7) Ab(G)

179

FOR ME TO LIVE IS CHRIST

Words and Music: J. White
Arr. Norman Warren

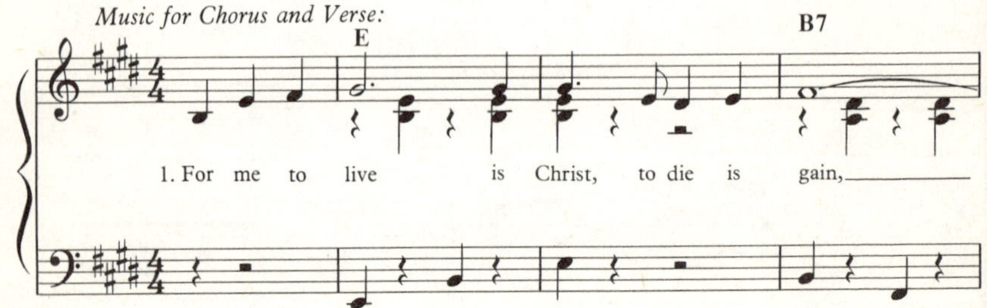
Music for Chorus and Verse:
E
B7
1. For me to live is Christ, to die is gain,_

E
to hold his hand, and walk his nar-row way;
E7
A
there is no peace, no joy, no thrill, like walk-ing in his
Am
E
F♯m7
B7
E
will for me to live is Christ, to die is gain.

2 Now once my heart was full of sin and shame,
till someone told me Jesus came to save;
when he said 'Come home to me!'
he set my poor heart free –
for me to live is Christ, to die is gain.

3 Now there are things that I still do not know,
but of this one thing I'm completely sure:
he who called me on that day,
washed all my sin away –
for me to live is Christ, to die is gain!

4 For me to live is Christ, to die is gain,
to hold his hand, and walk his narrow way;
there is no peace, no joy, no thrill,
like walking in his will –
for me to live is Christ, to die is gain.

180

FROM THE DISTANT EAST

(Is. 43: 1-6, 18-20. Mt. 3: 2-3)

C. R. Vaughan
Whitfield Jn. School, Liverpool 6

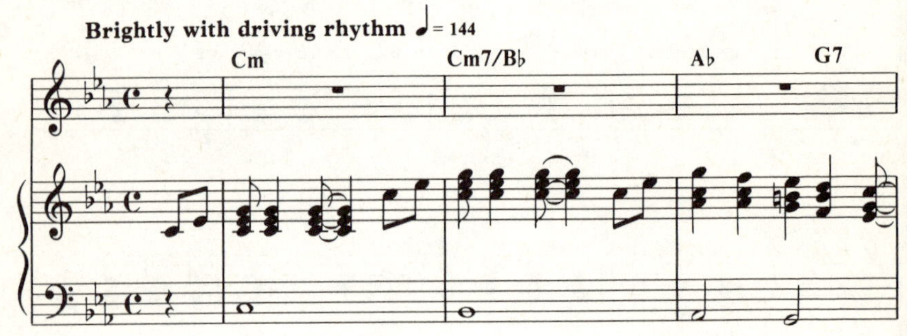
Brightly with driving rhythm ♩ = 144
Cm
Cm7/B♭
A♭
G7

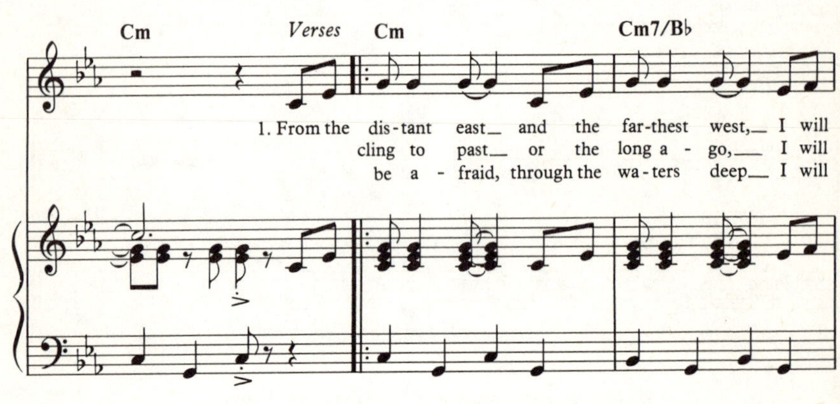
Cm
Verses
Cm
Cm7/B♭
1. From the dis-tant east_ and the far-thest west,_ I will
cling to past_ or the long a - go,_ I will
be a - fraid, through the wa-ters deep_ I will

A♭
G
Cm
Cm
bring my peo-ple home._ Let my peo-ple re-turn_ from the
bring my peo-ple home._ I will make_ a road_ and the
bring my peo-ple home._ Do not be_ a-fraid,_ as you

Cm7/B♭ A♭ G Cm
dis - tant lands,_ I will bring my peo-ple home._
ri - vers flow;_ I will bring my peo-ple home._
pass through fire_ I will bring my peo-ple home._
Cm
Chorus
Some-one is shout - ing in the des-ert, "Pre -
A♭ B♭ E♭ G7
-pare a road for the Lord;_
Cm
Make a path straight for him to tra - vel! Pre -

A♭ B♭ C G7

-pare a road for the Lord.___ Turn a-way from your sins."_

Cm

1&2

2. Do not
3. Do not

3

G7 Cm

Turn a-way from your sins,___

G7 Cm F Cm F G7 Cm

Turn a-way from your sins.___

181

GO, TELL IT ON THE MOUNTAIN

Traditional

G
Em
Am7
D7
G
C
G
Go, tell it on the moun - tain, o - ver the hills and ev - ery - where;
8 8
to Continue
Em
E♭
Am
Bm
D7
G
go, tell it on the moun - tain that Je - sus Christ is Lord! 1. O
8 8 8
Last time
G
C
G
D
A7
D7
Lord! when I was a seek - er I sought both night and
G
C
G
Am
A7
D7
D.C.
day I asked the Lord to help me, and he showed me the way:

2 Then he made me a watchman,
upon the city wall,
to tell of his salvation,
for Jesus died for all:
Go, tell it on the mountain . . .

3 Go tell it to your neighbour
in darkness here below,
go with the words of Jesus,
that all the world may know:
Go, tell it on the mountain . . .

GOD FORGAVE MY SIN

Carol Owens
Arr. Norman Warren

E B7 C♯m F♯m B7
1. God for – gave my sin in Je – sus' name — I've been
2. All power is given in Je – sus' name — in

F♯m B B7 E B7 E E7
born a – gain in Je – sus' name, and in
earth and heaven in Je – sus' name, and in

A E B7 E
Je – sus' name I come to you to

C♯m E A B7 E slowly
share his love as he told me to: He said,
(power)

a tempo
A
B7
'Free – ly, free – ly you have re – ceived —

E
free – ly, free – ly give!

C♯m
F♯m
B
Go in my name and be — cause you be — lieve

E
Oth – ers will know that I live.'

GOD HAS SPOKEN

Words: W. F. Jabusch
Israeli Folk Song
Arr. Norman Warren

Chorus
Am
E
God has spo - ken to his peo - ple, Al - le - lu - ia, —
Am Fine
and his words are words of wis - dom, Al - le - lu - ia!
Verse
E
E7
Am
E
1. O - pen your ears O Christ - ian peo - ple, O - pen your ears and
hear good news; O - pen your hearts O

Am
Dm
E
roy – al priest – hood, God has come _ to __ you. ____

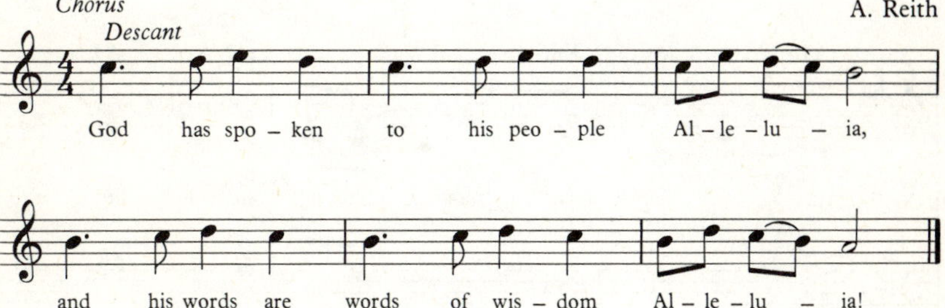
Chorus
Descant
A. Reith
God has spo – ken to his peo – ple Al – le – lu – ia,
and his words are words of wis – dom Al – le – lu – ia!

2 He who has ears to hear his message,
he who has ears, then let him hear;
he who would learn the way of wisdom,
let him hear God's word, let him hear God's word!
God has spoken . . .

3 Israel, come to greet the saviour!
Judah is glad to see his day;
from east and west the peoples travel,
he will show the way, he will show the way.
God has spoken . . .

THE GREATEST THING

M. Pendergrass
Arr. D. Peacock

D
Bm
Em
1. The great-est thing in all my life is know-ing you;
A7
Em
Em7/A
A7
the great-est thing in all my life is
Dsus
D
G/D
D
G
G/A
know-ing you. I want to know you
Dmaj7
Em7
A7
D
more, I want to know you more: the

Bm
Em
Em/A
D
great-est thing ______ in all my life is know – ing you.

2 The greatest thing in all my life is loving you;
the greatest thing in all my life is loving you.
I want to love you more,
I want to love you more:
the greatest thing in all my life is loving you.

3 The greatest thing in all my life is serving you;
the greatest thing in all my life is serving you.
I want to serve you more,
I want to serve you more:
the greatest thing in all my life is to serve you more.

HAPPINESS IS

Ira F. Stamphill
Arr. Norman Warren

Country and Western
E
F♯m
B7
1. Hap-pi-ness is to know the Sav-iour, liv-ing a life with-
E
A
in his fa-vour, hav-ing a change in my be-ha-viour—
1
2
E
B7
E
B7
E
Last time to Coda
hap-pi-ness is the Lord.
Lord.
v.3 Real
A
G♯m
C♯m
D♯m
G♯m
joy is mine, no mat-ter if tears may start; I've

C♯m
F♯m
F♯
found the se - cret — Je - sus in my

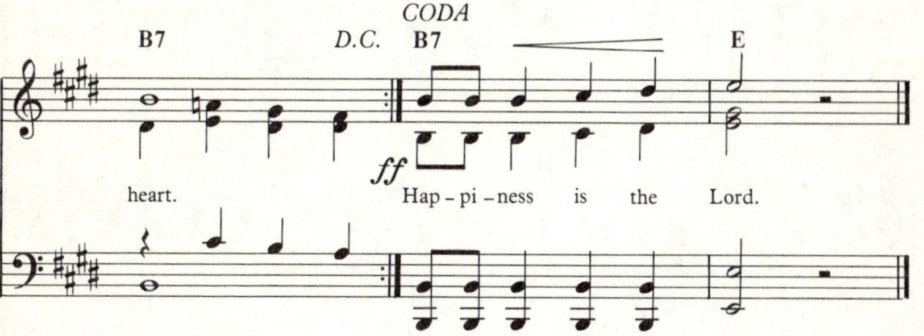
CODA
B7
D.C.
B7
E
ff
heart.
Hap - pi - ness is the Lord.

2 Happiness is a new creation,
'Jesus and me' in close relation,
having a part in his salvation —
happiness is the Lord.

3 Real joy is mine,
no matter if tears may start;
I've found the secret —
Jesus in my heart.

4 Happiness is to be forgiven,
living a life that's worth the living,
taking the road that leads to heaven —
happiness is the Lord,
happiness is the Lord!

HELP ME TO KNOW YOU

Words and Music by Don Marsh

A7 D A7 Em A7
1. Help me to know you as I once knew you, help me to seek you as I once
2. Turn me from sin: now I would be ho – ly, in true re – pen-tance I hum-bly
D D.S. D7 G
sought you; help me to love you as I once loved you bring me back
come; all that I am now and ev – er will be, I glad – ly sur –
D.S. love you as I once loved you, bring me back
D/A A7 D Fine Chorus G
close, Lord, clos – er to you:
– ren – der in – to your care:
close, Lord, clos – er to you.
Clos – er to you, Lord, clos – er to
D.S. al Fine
D F♯7/C♯ Bm E7 Em7 Gm/E A7
you, for I have wan – dered so far from your lov – ing voice; I want to

187

I AM COVERED OVER

The 'Cheam' Fellowship
Arr. David Peacock

(Capo 1)
E
Emaj7
A
G♯m7
I am covered ov - er with the robe of right-eousness that Je-sus gives to me —
F♯m7
B7
F♯m
F♯m♭5
gives to me; — I am cov-ered ov-er with the pre-cious blood of Je-sus and he
E
F♯m9
E
F♯m7
B7
E
lives in me — lives in me: — What a joy it is to know my
Emaj7
E7
A
G♯m7
F♯m
B7
heaven-ly Fa-ther loves me so! He gives to me ___ my Je - sus;
E
F♯m
B7
F♯m/E
E
when he looks at me he sees not what I used to be, but he sees Je - sus.

188

I AM WEAK BUT YOU ARE STRONG

Traditional
Arr. Norman Warren

C Dm G7
1. I am weak but you are strong, Je – sus keep me from all
C C7 F Dm7
wrong; I'll be sat – is – fied as long as I
G7 C C
v. 1-3
Last Chorus
walk, let me walk close with you. you.
Ped.

Alternative arrangement

Trad.
Arr. David Peacock

Quite Slow

C A7 Dm7 G7

1. I am weak but you are strong,

(smooth bass)

Dm7 G7 C
Je – sus keep me from all wrong;
C C7 F
I'll be sat – is – fied as long as I
C Dm7 G7 C C
Repeat for Chorus
Last time
walk, let me walk close with you.
be.

Just a closer walk with you
all of life's long journey through;
let it be that all I do
honours you, dear Lord, honours you.

2 In this world of toils and snares,
if I falter, Lord, who cares;
who with me my burden shares? —
none but you, dear Lord, none but you:
Just a closer walk . . .

3 When my feeble life is o'er,
time for me will be no more:
guide me gently, safely home,
to your kingdom's shore, to that shore:
Just a closer walk . . .

Use chords when accompaniment is by Guitar only

189

I HAVE DECIDED

Unknown
Arr. Norman Warren

C
F6 C
1. I have de - cid - ed to fol - low Je - sus, I have de -
2. The cross be - fore me, the world be - hind me, The cross be -

F
C
G
Em
- cid - ed to fol - low Je - sus, I have de - cid - ed to fol - low
- fore me, the world be - hind me, The cross be - fore me, the world be -

F6
C
Am
D7
G7
C
Je - sus — no turn - ing back, ——— no turn - ing back.
- hind me — no turn - ing back, ——— no turn - ing back.

190

I WANT TO LIVE FOR JESUS

Unknown
Arr. Norman Warren

C
1. I want to live for Je – sus ev – ery day, ev – ery day
I want to live for Je – sus come what may, come what may:

F
C
A7
Take the world and all its plea – sure! I've got a more en – dur – ing trea – sure,

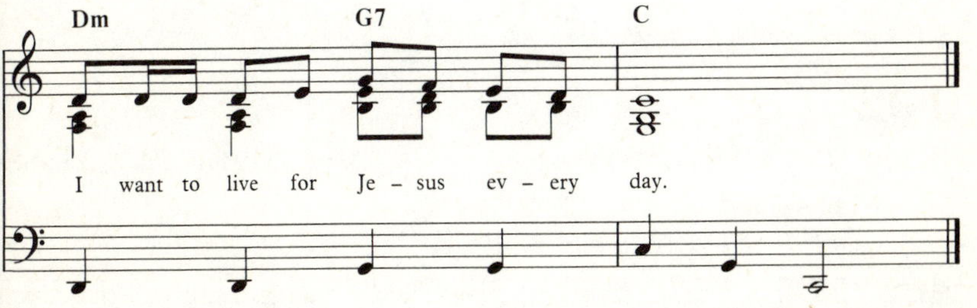
Dm
G7
C
I want to live for Je – sus ev – ery day.

Alternative verse: 'I'm going to live for Jesus . . .'

191

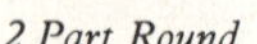

I WAS LOST BUT JESUS FOUND ME

Unknown
Arr. Norman Warren

2 Part Round

1.
G C Am D G
1. I was lost but Je-sus found me, found the sheep that went a-stray. Threw his
2. Glo-ry, glo-ry, al-le-lu-ia, come and bless the Lord our King, Glo-ry,

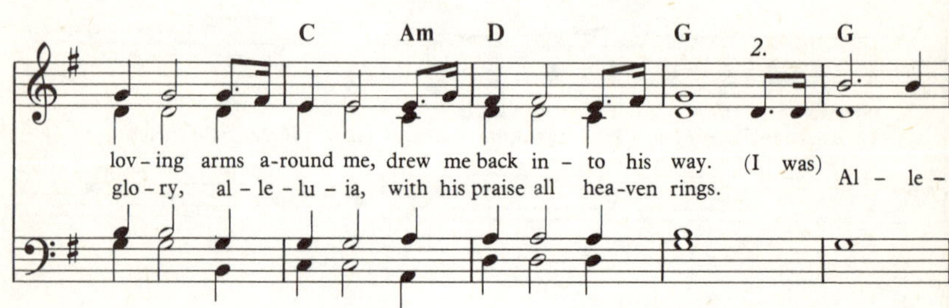
C Am D G 2. G
lov-ing arms a-round me, drew me back in-to his way. (I was)
glo-ry, al-le-lu-ia, with his praise all hea-ven rings.
Al - le -

C D G C Am D G
-lu-ia, Al-le-lu-ia, Al-le-lu-ia, Al-le-lu-ia, Glo-ry

192

IF ANY MAN WILL FOLLOW

Words and Music: M. A. Baughen

With vigour

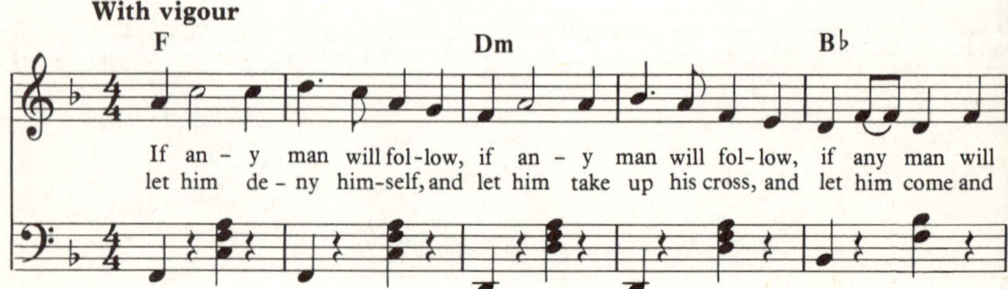
F Dm B♭
If an-y man will fol-low, if an-y man will fol-low, if any man will
let him de-ny him-self, and let him take up his cross, and let him come and

THE CHRISTIAN LIFE
To Coda (last time)
1
2
C7 F C7 F C7 F
fol - low af - ter my Je - sus, Lord!
fol - low af - ter my
C7 F
Who - so - ev - er will live for self will throw his life a - way — Christ gives
Who - so - ev - er will be a-shamed of Je - sus and his words, in this
G7 C C7
life to all who fol - low him.
sin - ful age in which we live,
What is a man ad - van-taged if he
Je-sus the king will be a-shamed of
F Dm7 G7 C7
gains the whole wide world and then los - es his soul!
him in that great day, when in glo - ry he comes!
D.C.
Last time only
Dm F G9 B♭m7 A♭m Dm7 Cm7 C7 F
Let him come and fol - low af - ter my Lord!

193

IF I TRIED

Words and Music: J. McKenzie
Arr. Norman Warren

D
A
1. If I tried to live for you Lord, to - day; if

A7
D
D7
I tried to fol - low your won - der - ful way, then

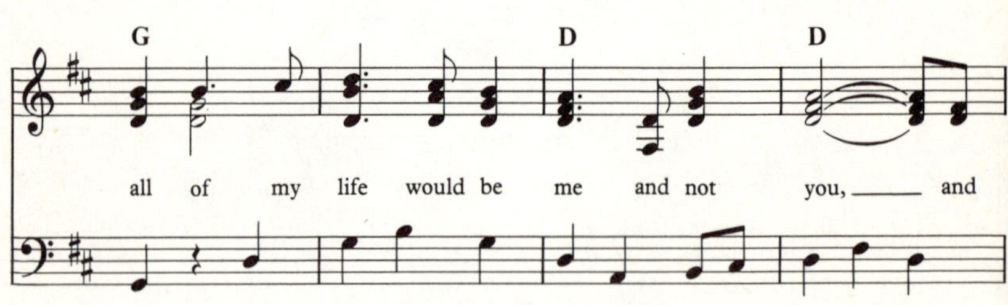
G
D
D
all of my life would be me and not you, and

A7
A7
D
none of your glo - ry would ev - er shine through.

1 & 2
A7
D
A7
3
D
G
D
you.

Melody for 2nd verse begins:

Since I first met you, I knew, Lord, you were the way,

2 Since I first met you, I knew Lord you were the way,
I tried hard to walk in your footsteps each day,
but somehow my life didn't glorify you —
so make me your channel in all that I do.

3 Take each new day, whatever's in store,
take my whole being and into me pour,
your power and your Spirit — O make me anew,
for no one can change me, Lord Jesus, but you.

194

IF MY PEOPLE

Words: SU Switzerland (from 2 Chronicles 7)
Music: Cyril Squire
Arr. David Peacock

Dm Gm C7
If my peo – ple will be hum – bled, and

F7 B♭ Gm
pray and seek my pre – sence and re – pent of all their

A7 Dm C7 [1] F D7
e – vil, 1. then from hea-ven I will hear. If my
2. then will I for-give their

[2] F A B♭ C7 F
sin and give heal – ing to their land.

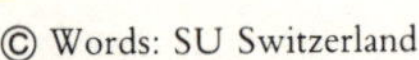

195

IN MY LIFE, LORD

Bob Kilpatrick
Arr. D. Peacock

Ladies
C G Am C
1. In my life, Lord,
Men (Melody)
Dm B♭ G7 C G
be glo - ri - fied, be glo - ri - fied: in my
Am C Dm G7 C
life, Lord, be glo - ri - fied to - day!

Alternative verses: 2 In my song . . .

3 In your church . . .

4 In my speech . . .

etc.

196

IN YOUR WAY AND IN YOUR TIME

Graham Kendrick
Arr. M. Evans

Slowly

C G C F

1. In your way___ and in your time___ that's how it's

C Am Dm

going to be in my life;___

G E Am

and in your per - fect way I'll rest my wear - y

Dm G

mind,___ and as you lead I'll fol - low close be -

C E Am

- hind:___ and in your pre - sence I will know your peace is

Dm7
G
mine in your
time
there is
C
Dm
C
F
C
Dm
rest,
there is
rest.
1, 2.
Last time
C
F
C
F
C
In your

2 In your way and in your time —
that's how it's going to be in my life;
dear Jesus soothe me now
till all my strivings cease,
kiss me with the beauty of your peace:
and I will wait and not be anxious at the time —
in your time there is rest, there is rest.

3 In your way and in your time —
that's how it's going to be in my life;
and though some prayers I've prayed
may seem unanswered yet,
you never come too quickly or too late:
and I will wait and I will not regret the time —
in your time there is rest, there is rest.

197

THE LORD HAS SAID

Words: Christopher Idle
Music: Norman Warren

Em7 Am Em7 Am Em7 F Am Dm Em7
1. The Lord has said that he will be our God and we shall be his
Am Am7 Dm Fmaj7 G A
peo - ple: for he writes on our hearts all the words of his law; he for -
C Em7 F Dm E E7 Am G
- gives all our sin and re - mem-bers it no more: and this is God's new
1 2
F Am Em7 Am Dm E7 Am Am
cov-en-ant with us in Je - sus Christ our Lord. and Lord.

2 Step out in faith that he will be our God
and we shall be his people:
for the lost are restored,
from the west to the east;
we shall all know the Lord
from the greatest to the least:
and this is God's new covenant with us
in Jesus Christ our Lord:

And this is God's new covenant with us
in Jesus Christ our Lord.

THE LORD MY SHEPHERD

Words: Christopher Idle
Music: Merla Watson
Arr. Norman Warren

Verses 1, 3, 5
Em B7 Em Em Am Em B7 Em Am Em B7 Em
FINE
1. The Lord my shep-herd rules my life and gives me all I need; he
leads me by re-fresh-ing streams, in pas-tures green I
feed. 2. The Lord re-vives my fail-ing strength, he makes my joy com-
-plete and in right paths, for his name's sake he guides my falter-ing feet.

3 Though in a valley dark as death,
no evil makes me fear;
your shepherd's staff protects my way,
for you are with me there.

4 While all my enemies look on
you spread a royal feast;
you fill my cup, anoint my head,
and treat me as your guest.

5 Your goodness and your gracious love
pursue me all my days;
your house , O Lord, shall be my home —
your name, my endless praise.

6 To Father, Son and Spirit, praise!
to God, whom we adore,
be worship, glory, power and love,
both now and evermore!

199

MINE ARE THE HANDS

Howard Guinness

D A7 Bm D G6 A7 G D
Mine are the hands to do the work,

Bm E7 A A7 D
my feet shall run for thee, my lips shall sound the

A7 D G Em B7 Em D A7 G D
glo - rious news— Lord, here am I, send me!

Version 1 Mine are the hands to do the work,
your servant I will be,
my lips shall sound the glorious news —
Lord, here am I, send me!

Version 2 Mine are the hands to do the work,
my feet shall run for thee,
my lips shall sound the glorious news —
Lord, here am I, send me!

200

O SINNER MAN

Trad.
Arr. Norman Warren

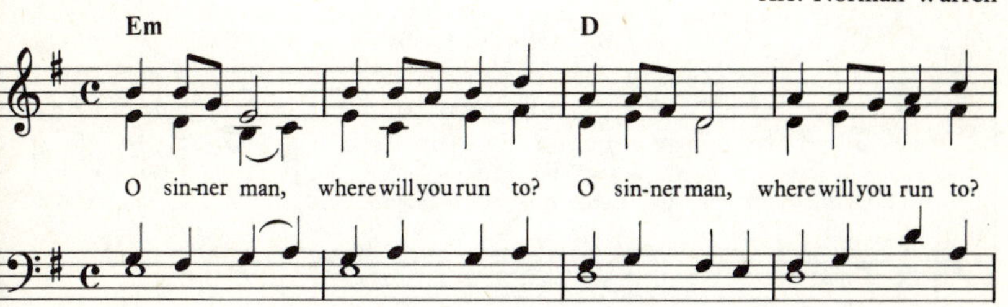
Em
D
O sin-ner man, where will you run to? O sin-ner man, where will you run to?

Em
Am
Bm7
Em
O sin-ner man, where will you run to? all on that day?

1 Run to the rocks - 'Rocks won't you hide me?'
run to the rocks - 'Rocks won't you hide me?'
run to the rocks - 'Rocks won't you hide me?'
all on that day:
O Sinner man . . .

2 Run to the sea - sea is a-boiling,
run to the sea - sea is a-boiling,
run to the sea - sea is a-boiling,
all on that day:
O Sinner man . . .

3 Run to the Lord - 'Lord won't you hide me?'
run to the Lord - 'Lord won't you hide me?'
run to the Lord - 'Lord won't you hide me?'
all on that day:
O Sinner man . . .

4 O Sinner man, should been a-praying,
O Sinner man, should been a-praying,
O Sinner man, should been a-praying,
all on that day:
O Sinner man . . .

201

O THE LOVE

Estelle White

C F B♭ C7 F B♭ F C F
1. O, the love of my Lord is the es - sence ___ of ___ all that I

B♭ C7 F B♭ F Am B♭ C
love here on earth! ___ All the beau - ty I see he has giv - en to

Last time
Dm C7 F B♭ C F B♭ F F
me, and his giv - ing is gen - tle as si - lence. ___

2 Every day, every hour, every moment
have been blessed by the strength of his love:
at the turn of each tide
he is there at my side,
and his touch is as gentle as silence.

3 There've been times when I've turned from his presence,
and I've walked other paths, other ways:
but I've called on his name
in the dark of my shame,
and his mercy was gentle as silence.

202

O WHEN THE SAINTS GO MARCHING IN

Traditional
Arr. D. G. Wilson

F
1. O when the saints go marching in, O when the
(O when the saints)
(go marching in)

Gm C7 F F7
saints go march-ing in; O Lord I want to be a-mong the

B♭ Gm Am7 B♭maj7 F6 C9 F
num-ber when the saints go march-ing in!

2 O when they crown him Lord of all,
O when they crown him Lord of all;
O Lord, I want to be among the number
when they crown him Lord of all.

3 O when all knees bow at his name,
O when all knees bow at his name;
O Lord, I want to be among the number
when all knees bow at his name.

4 O when they sing the saviour's praise,
O when they sing the saviour's praise;
O Lord, I want to be among the number
when they sing the saviour's praise.

5 O when the saints go marching in,
O when the saints go marching in;
O Lord, I want to be among the number
when the saints go marching in!

203

PEACE IS FLOWING

Unknown
Arr. D. Peacock

E
B7
E
1. Peace is flow-ing like a riv - er, —
F♯m7
B7
E
B7
flow - ing out through you and me, —
E
B7
E
spread - ing out in - to the des - ert,

F♯m7
B7
E
A
E
set – ting all the cap-tives free: Let it
Chorus
A
B7
E
G♯m7
C♯7
flow through me, let it flow through me, let the
F♯m7
Bsus
B7
1
E
F♯m7
E
2
E
B7
E
migh-ty love of God flow out through me! Let it out through me.

Alternative verses: 2 Joy is flowing like a river . . .

3 Love is flowing like a river . . .

4 Hope is flowing like a river . . .

204

SEEK YE FIRST

Karen Lafferty

2 Part Round

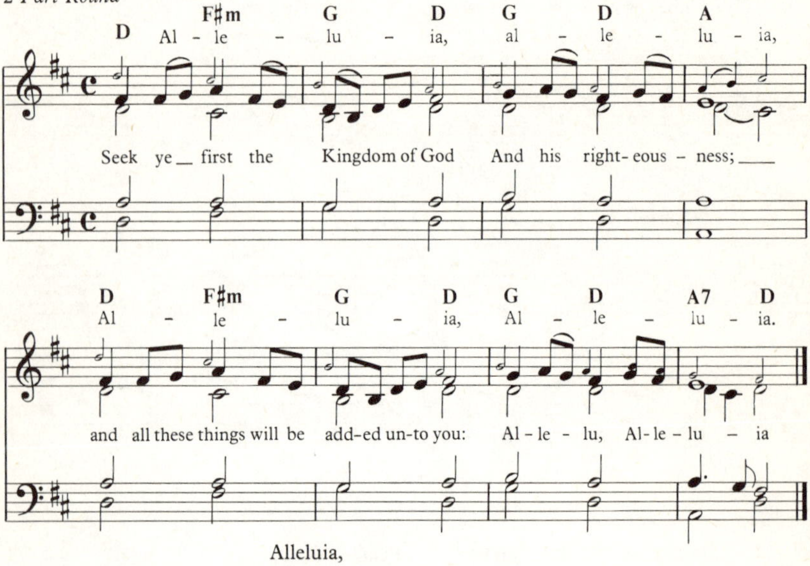

D F♯m G D G D A
Al - le - lu - ia, al - le - lu - ia,

Seek ye first the Kingdom of God And his right-eous - ness;

D F♯m G D G D A7 D
Al - le - lu - ia, Al - le - lu - ia.

and all these things will be add-ed un-to you: Al - le - lu, Al - le - lu - ia

Alleluia,
alleluia,
alleluia,
alleluia!

Ask and it shall be given unto you,
seek and ye shall find;
knock and it shall be opened unto you:
allelu, alleluia!

Alleluia . . !

The second verse is not part of the song as originally written. Its origin is unknown.

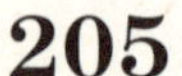
205

SOON AND VERY SOON

Andrae Crouch

F
B♭/F
F
1. Soon and ver - y soon we are go-ing to see the King,
2. No more cry - in' there we are go-ing to see the King,
3. No more dy - in' there we are go-ing to see the King,
4. Soon and ver - y soon we are go-ing to see the King,

C7 F
soon and ver - y soon we are go-ing to see the King,
no more cry - in' there we are go-ing to see the King,
no more dy - in' there we are go-ing to see the King,
soon and ver - y soon we are go-ing to see the King,
F F
soon and ver - y soon we are go-ing to see the King,
no more cry - in' there we are go-ing to see the King,
no more dy - in' there we are go-ing to see the King,
soon and ver - y soon we are go-ing to see the King,
F7 Gm Bb Bbm F C C7 F
al - le - lu - ia, al - le - lu - ia, we're going to see the King!
1,2 3,4
G7 C7 F G7 C7
al - le - lu - ia, al - le - lu -
F Softer G7 C7 F G7 C7 Fine 4th x
- ia, al - le - lu - ia, al - le - lu - ia.

206

THE STEADFAST LOVE OF THE LORD

Edith McNeill
Arr. David Peacock

Chorus

B9 E F♯m B7 E B7 B9

The stead-fast love of the Lord nev-er ceas – es, his mer – cies

E F♯m G♯m C♯m F♯m B7

nev – er ___ come to an end; ______ they are new ev-ery morn-ing

G♯m C♯m F♯m Bsus B7 E B7 E7

new ev-ery morn-ing: Great is your faith – ful – ness, O Lord!

Verse 1 only
A E B7 E A C♯7 F♯m7
Great is your faith – ful – ness! 1. The Lord is my port – ion, says my

B7 E7 A F♯m B7
soul, ___ there – fore I will hope in him.
vs. 2, 3, 4. A G♯m C♯m F♯m B7 v.4
2. The Lord ___ is good to those who wait for him, to the soul that
3. The Lord will not cast ___ off for ev – er, but will have com –
4. So let us ex – am – ine ___ all our ways, and re – turn to the
E E7 A
seeks him: it is good ___ that we should wait ___
– pass – ion: for he does ___ not will – ing –
Lord: ___ let us lift up our hearts and ___
G♯m C♯m F♯7 B7
qui – et – ly for the sal – va – tion of the Lord.
– ly af – flict or grieve the ___ sons ___ of ___ men.
hands ___ to ___ God ___ in ___ heaven.

207

THE SUMMER HAS GONE

Words: Margaret Bowdler
Music: Greig
Arr. Norman Warren

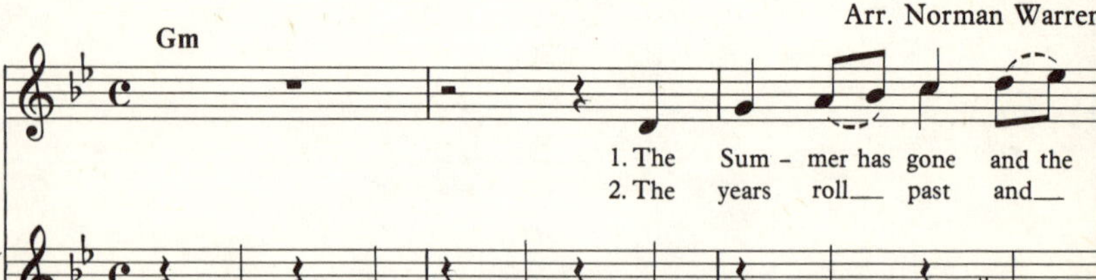
Gm
1. The Sum - mer has gone and the
2. The years roll__ past and__

D
Gm
Au-tumn turns to gold, the__ Au-tumn turns to gold;__ the
mor - tal man must die, and__ mor - tal man must die;__ for

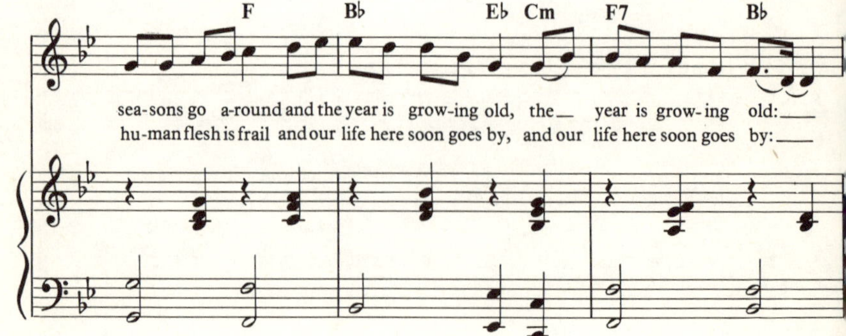
F
B♭
E♭ Cm
F7
B♭
sea-sons go a-round and the year is grow-ing old, the__ year is grow-ing old:__
hu-man flesh is frail and our life here soon goes by, and our life here soon goes by:__

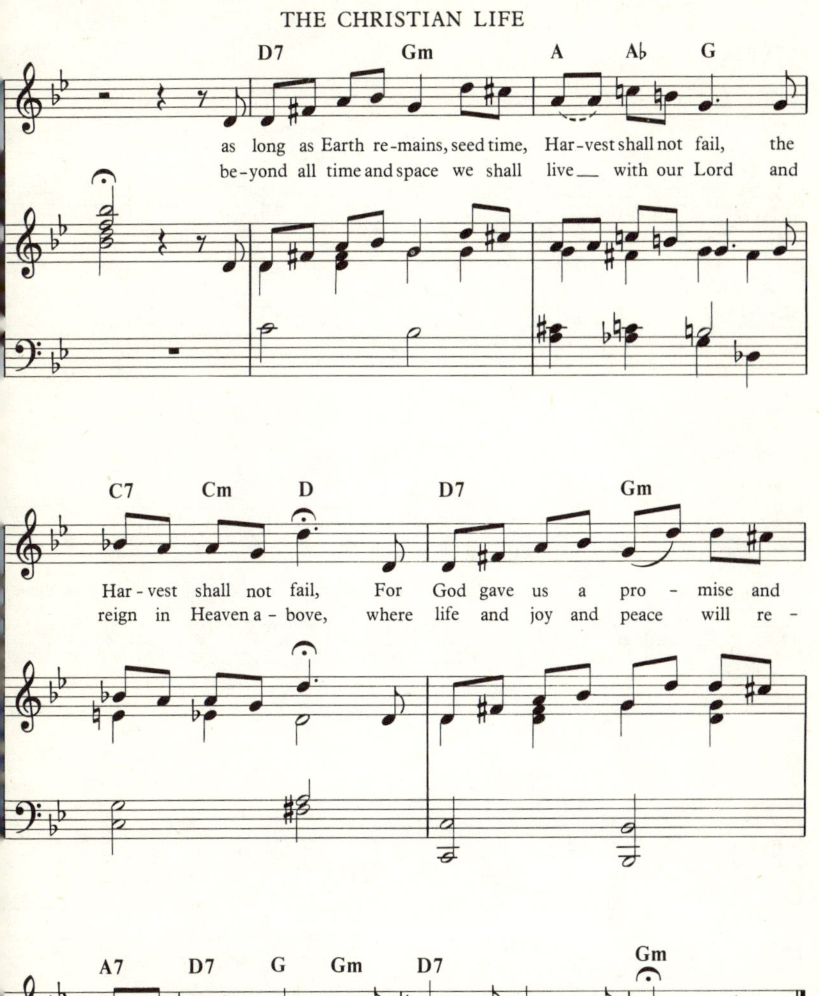
D7 Gm A A♭ G
as long as Earth re-mains, seed time, Har-vest shall not fail, the
be-yond all time and space we shall live__ with our Lord and
C7 Cm D D7 Gm
Har-vest shall not fail, For God gave us a pro - mise and
reign in Heaven a - bove, where life and joy and peace will re -

A7 D7 G Gm D7 Gm

God's word shall pre - vail, and God's word shall pre - vail.

- main and no more pain— a king - dom filled with love.

208

TELL ME WHY DO YOU WEEP?

Graham Kendrick
Arr. M. Evan

Chorus
Am
Tell me why do you weep? Tell me why do you mourn? Tell me why do you

E
Am
look so sad? Tell me why don't you dance? Tell me why don't you

E
Verse
Am
sing? Tell me why don't you look to the sky? 1. Don't you know that you

E
Am
E
King is com - ing? Don't you know that your King is nigh?

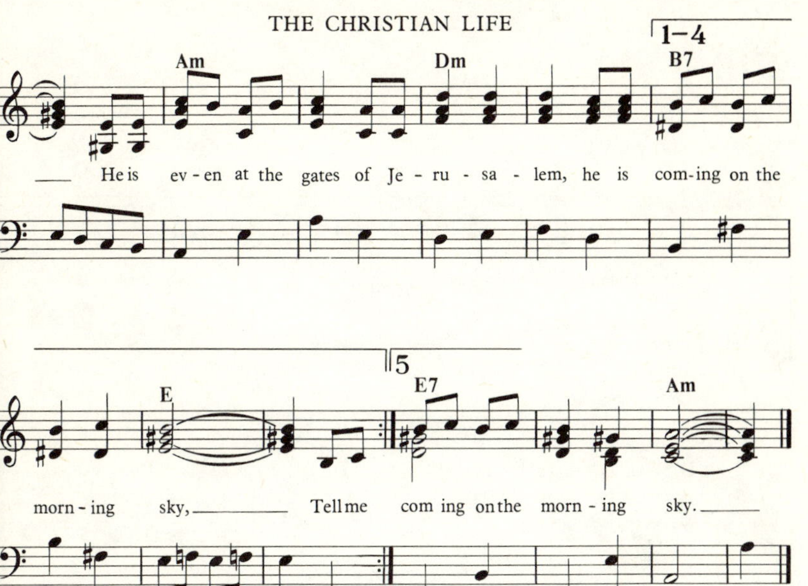
1–4
Am
Dm
B7
He is ev - en at the gates of Je - ru - sa - lem, he is com-ing on the
5
E
E7
Am
morn - ing sky, Tell me com ing on the morn - ing sky.

2 Don't you know that the feast is ready,
ready for the bride to come?
Brothers, keep your lamps a-burning —
the ending of the age is come.
Tell me . . .

3 Don't you know you are the Lord's invited?
Don't you know you are the chosen ones?
You in whom he has delighted
shall rise with Jesus when he comes.
Tell me . . .

4 Come arise, my love, my fairest daughter:
the winter and the rain are gone,
the flowers of summer are appearing,
the time of singing songs has come.
Tell me . . .

5 Don't you know that your king is coming?
Don't you know that your king is nigh?
He is even at the gates of Jerusalem,
he is coming on the morning sky.

209

THANKS BE TO GOD

Robert Stoodley
Arr. D. Peacock

Chorus
D G A D G A7
Thanks be to God who gives us the
D G D G A7 F#7 Bm
vic - to - ry, gives us the vic - to - ry through
1 2
Em A Em A D
our Lord Je - sus Christ; our Lord Je - sus Christ.
Verses
D G A D
1. He is a - ble to keep us from fall - ing and to

G
A7
D
G
set
us
free from
sin;
so let us each live
A
D
G
D
A
D
up to our call - ing and com-mit
our
way
to him:

2 Jesus knows all about our temptations —
he has had to bear them too;
he will show us how to escape them,
if we trust him he will lead us through:
Thanks be to God . . !

3 He has led us from the power of darkness
to the kingdom of his blessed Son;
so let us join in praise together
and rejoice in what the Lord has done:
Thanks be to God . . !

4 Praise the Lord for sending Jesus
to the Cross of Calvary:
now he's risen, reigns in power
and death is swallowed up in victory:
Thanks be to God . . !

210

THERE'S A WORLD OUT THERE

Unknown
Music: Norman Warren

Unison
E
A
E
1. There's a world out there, the Lord calls you to lis - ten,
3. There's a world out there, the Lord calls you to serve him,

C♯m
F♯m
E
A6
B
There's a world out there, don't you hear it cry,
There's a world out there, don't you hear his call,

E
G♯m
C♯m
There's a world out there, won't you stop and lis - ten,
There's a world out there, won't you go out for him,

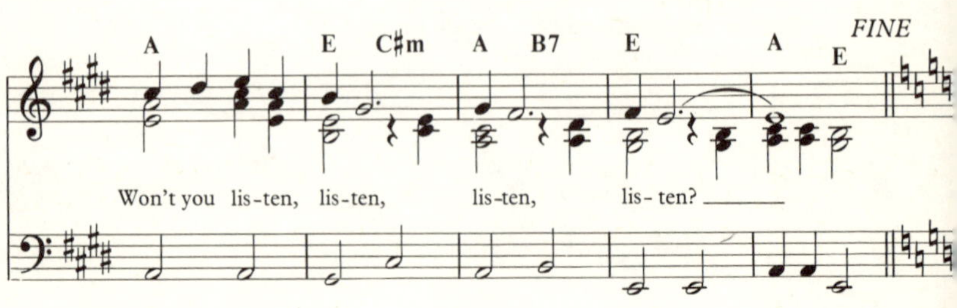
A
E
C♯m
A
B7
E
A
E
FINE
Won't you lis-ten, lis-ten, lis-ten, lis- ten?

C
Em
F
G7
2. There's a world out there, don't you hear it cry - ing,

C
Em
Gm
Am
There's a world out there don't you hear it sigh - ing,

C
F
Em
Am
There's a world out there, don't you hear it dy - ing,

F
Em
Am
Dm
G7
C
F
C
B7
Won't you lis - ten, lis - ten, lis - ten, lis - ten?

211

THIS WORLD IS NOT MY HOME

Traditional
Arr. G. R. Timms

G
G7
C
G
v. 3
1. This world is not my home, I'm just a - pass - ing through; my
A7
D
D7
G
Em
G
trea-sures are laid up some where be-yond the blue: the sav-iour beck-ons me from
C
G
C
G
A9
D
G
hea-ven's op - en door, and I can't feel at home in this world an - y more.
Chorus
Gm
Bm
Em
G
C
D
D7
G
O Lord, you know, I have no friend like you: if hea-ven's not my home then,

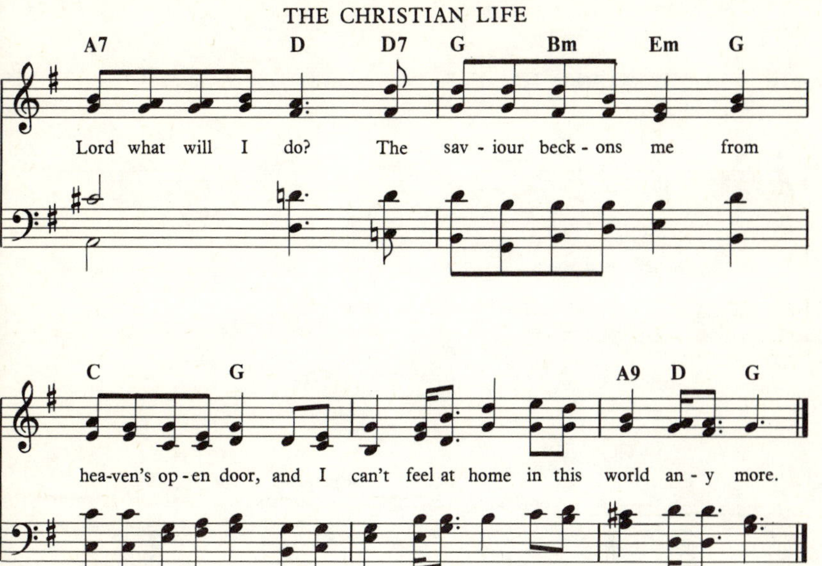
A7
D
D7
G
Bm
Em
G
Lord what will I do? The sav - iour beck - ons me from
C
G
A9
D
G
hea-ven's op - en door, and I can't feel at home in this world an - y more.

2 They're all expecting me,
and that's one thing I know,
my saviour pardoned me,
now onward I must go:
I know he'll take me through
though I am weak and poor,
and I can't feel at home
in this world any more.
O Lord, you know . . .

3 Just over in glory land
we'll live eternally,
the saints on every hand
are shouting victory:
their songs of sweetest praise
drift back from heaven's shore —
and I can't feel at home
in this world any more.
O Lord, you know . . .

THOUGH THE WORLD HAS FORSAKEN GOD

Words and Music: R. T. Bewes
Arr. M. C. T. Strover

E
E6 E
B7
1. Though the world has for - sa - ken God,_ treads a dif-ferent path,_ lives a
Ped.
Ped.
simile

E
Emaj7
E6 E
diff-'rent way, I walk the road that the sav - iour trod,_ and all may

B7
E
Chorus
know I live un - der Je - sus' sway._ They are watch-ing you,_ mark-ing

E9add6 E
B9
3
3
E6
all you do, hear - ing the things_ you say: let them

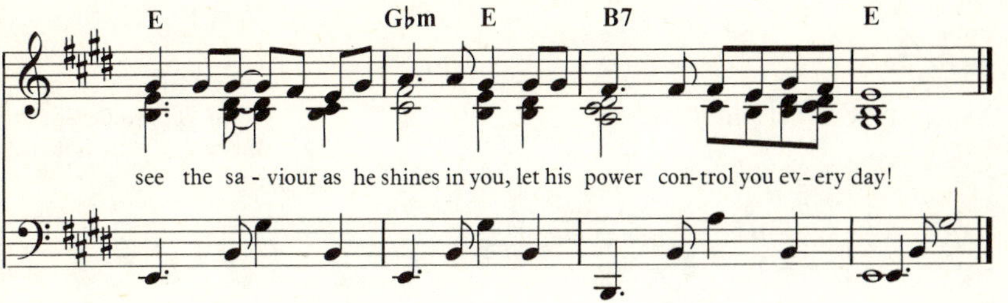
E
G♭m
E
B7
E
see the sa - viour as he shines in you, let his power con-trol you ev - ery day!

2 Men will look at the life I lead,
see the side I take, and the things I love;
they judge my Lord by my every deed —
Lord, set my affections on things above!
They are watching you . . .

3 When assailed in temptation's hour,
by besetting sins, by the fear of man,
then I can know Jesus' mighty power,
and become like him in his perfect plan.
They are watching you . . .

4 Here on earth people walk in night;
with no lamp to guide, they are dead in sin:
I know the Lord who can give them light,
I live, yet not I, but Christ within!
They are watching you . . .

213

TRUST IN THE LORD

Unknown

Round
Proverbs 3: 5–8

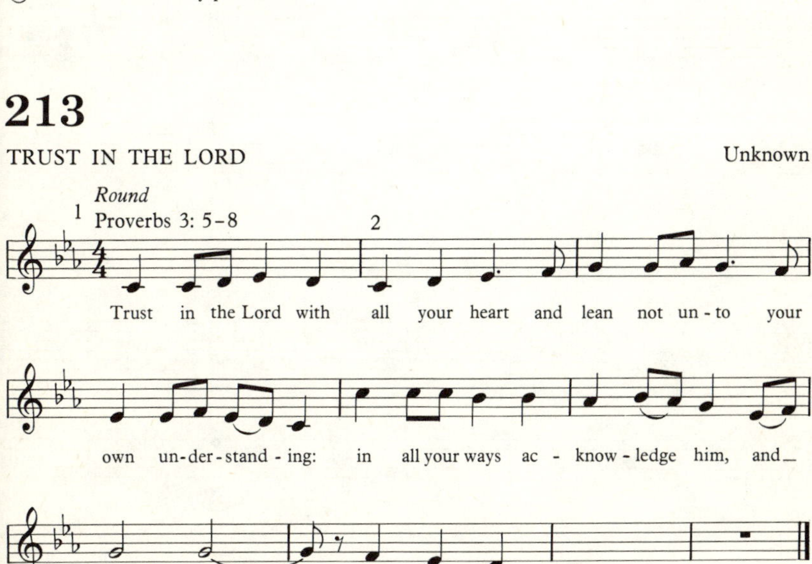
1
2
Trust in the Lord with all your heart and lean not un - to your
own un - der - stand - ing: in all your ways ac - know - ledge him, and
he shall di - rect your paths.

214

AS WATER TO THE THIRSTY

Words: T. Dudley-Smith
Music: T. Brian Coleman

1 As water to the thirsty,
as beauty to the eyes,
as strength that follows weakness,
as truth instead of lies,
as songtime and springtime
and summertime to be,
so is my Lord,
my living Lord,
so is my Lord to me.

2 Like calm in place of clamour,
like peace that follows pain,
like meeting after parting,
like sunshine after rain,
like moonlight and starlight
and sunlight on the sea,
so is my Lord,
my living Lord,
so is my Lord to me.

3 As sleep that follows fever,
as gold instead of grey,
as freedom after bondage,
as sunrise to the day,
as home to the traveller
and all he longs to see,
so is my Lord,
my living Lord,
so is my Lord to me.

215

WERE YOU THERE WHEN THEY CRUCIFIED MY LORD?

Traditional
Arr. Norman Warren

E
A
B7
C♯m
A
1. Were you there when they cru - ci - fied my Lord?

E
G♯m
A
E
F♯m
Were you there when they cru - ci - fied my Lord?

B
B7
E
A
E
E
E7
O
some - times it

A
E
C♯m
A
cau - ses me to trem - ble, trem - ble, trem - ble: were you

E
G♯m
A
B7
E
there when they cru - ci - fied my Lord?

2 Were you there when they nailed him to the tree?
Were you there when they nailed him to the tree?
O . . sometimes it causes me to tremble, tremble, tremble:
were you there when they nailed him to the tree?

3 Were you there when they pierced him in the side?
Were you there when they pierced him in the side?
O . . sometimes it causes me to tremble, tremble, tremble:
were you there when they pierced him in the side?

4 Were you there when the sun refused to shine?
Were you there when the sun refused to shine?
O . . sometimes it causes me to tremble, tremble, tremble:
were you there when the sun refused to shine?

5 Were you there when they laid him in the tomb?
Were you there when they laid him in the tomb?
O . . sometimes it causes me to tremble, tremble, tremble:
were you there when they laid him in the tomb?

6 Were you there when he rose up from the dead?
Were you there when he rose up from the dead?
O . . sometimes I feel like shouting 'Glory, glory, glory!' —
were you there when he rose up from the dead?

216

WHICH WAY ARE YOU CHOOSING?

Words and Music: R. T. Bewes
Arr. M. C. T. Strover

E A E
1. Which way are you choos - ing, the nar - row or broad? you'll
B7 E
have to make up your mind! Just give up your own way and
A E B7
fol - low the Lord: why don't you make up your
E A E
mind? He died, the strang - er of Ga - li - lee to

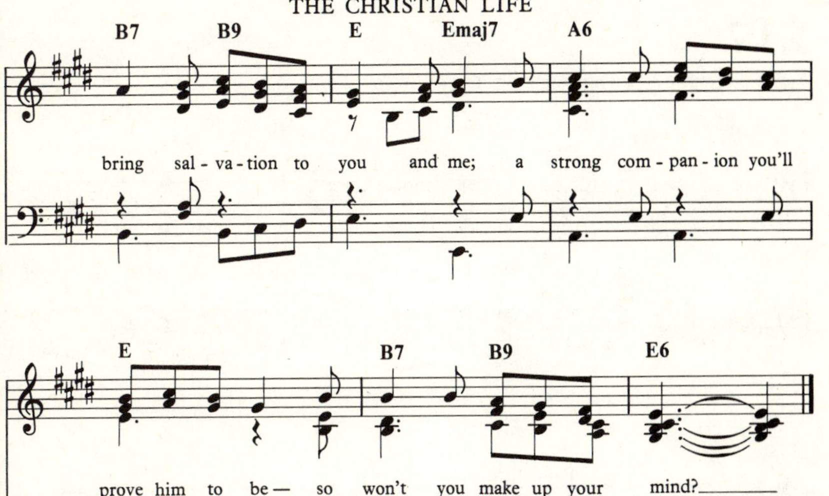
B7 B9 E Emaj7 A6
bring sal-va-tion to you and me; a strong com-pan-ion you'll
E B7 B9 E6
prove him to be — so won't you make up your mind?

2 Which crowd will you follow, the large or the small? —
be sure to make up your mind!
The cost is demanding, but hear Jesus call:
then come and make up your mind.
Your friends may shun you unthinkingly,
but Christ gives power and liberty;
to life with purpose you'll find the key,
when once you make up your mind.

3 On which are you resting, the rock or the sand? —
you'd better make up your mind!
With Christ as foundation your building will stand:
but have you made up your mind?
Temptations and trials must come your way,
the storms of judgement will rage one day:
take Jesus and on him your confidence stay —
don't wait, but make up your mind!

4 O what will you do with the saviour today? —
he bids you make up your mind!
Repent and accept him without delay,
O sinner, make up your mind!
Why stumble alone along the road?
He'll sort your tangles, he'll take your load,
and in your heart he will make his abode —
it's time to make up your mind!

217

YOU SHALL GO OUT WITH JOY

Stuart Dauermann
Arr. David Peacock

Isaiah 55: 12

Dm
You shall go out with joy, and be led forth with peace, and the

F
Gm7
C7
A7
moun-tains and the hills shall break forth be - fore you. There'll be

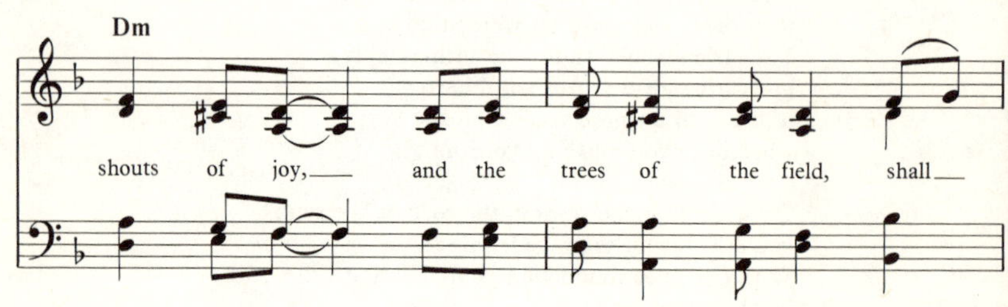
Dm
shouts of joy, and the trees of the field, shall

A7
Dm
F
clap, shall clap their hands. And the trees of the field shall

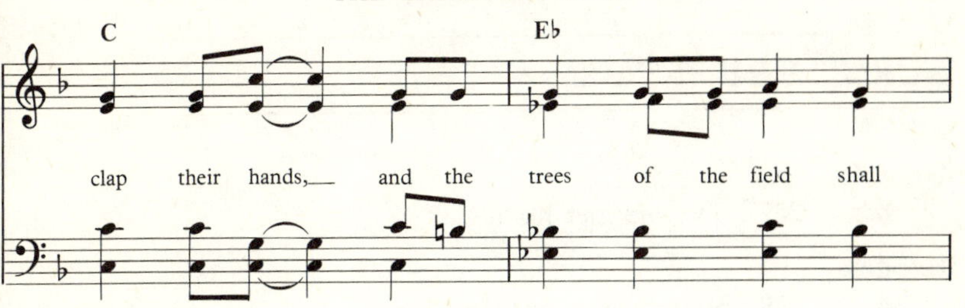
C
E♭
clap their hands, and the trees of the field shall

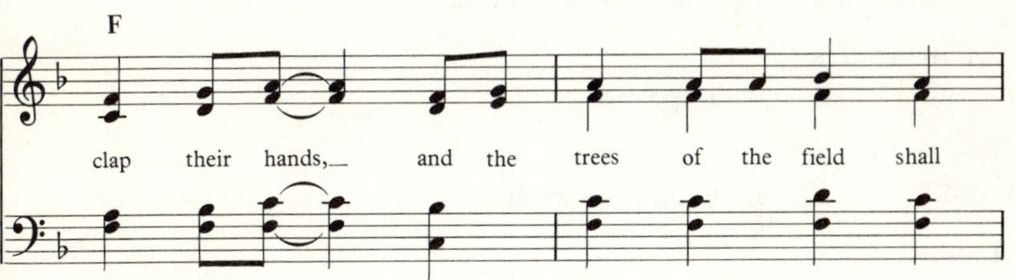
F
clap their hands, and the trees of the field shall

C
A7
Dm
clap their hands, and you'll go out with joy.

SCRIPTURE INDEX

Genesis

8	207	The summer has gone

Exodus

14	58	How great is our God

Numbers

6	147	To God's loving-kindness

2 Chronicles

7	194	If my people

Job

42	62	My God is so great

Psalms

19	119	Wonderful and marvellous
22	22	In the presence of your people
23	198	The Lord my shepherd
25	167	Unto you O Lord
37	206	The steadfast love of the Lord
46	153	Be still and know
47	7	Clap your hands (I)
	8	Clap your hands (II)
63	53	Your loving kindness
68	61	Let God arise
87	135	City, O city
89	59	I have made a covenant
95	14	Come sing praises
	26	Let us come into his presence
	27	Let us praise the Lord our God
98	39	Sing a new song
100	20	I will enter his gates
	25	Jubilate everybody
106	58	How great is our God
118	146	This is the day
119	119	Wonderful and marvellous
126	21	I will sing, I will sing
134	12	Come bless the Lord
136	29	O give thanks
137	172	By flowing waters
	173	By the waters

146	35	Praise the Lord
149	31	O praise the Lord
150	34	Praise the Lord in his holiness
Proverbs		
3	204	Seek ye first
	213	Trust in the Lord
24	119	Wonderful and marvellous
Song of Solomon		
2	93	Lord Jesus
	102	See him like a gazelle
	208	Tell me why do you weep?
Isaiah		
2	200	O sinner man
6	57	Holy, holy, holy, the Lord God is holy
	63	We see the Lord
	199	Mine are the hands
7	68	Emmanuel, Emmanuel
9	74	His name is higher
	120	You are the king of glory
26	168	You will keep him in perfect peace
40	37	Prepare the way of the Lord!
43	180	From the distant east
51	46	Therefore the redeemed
52	76	How lovely on the mountains
53	76	How lovely on the mountains
55	217	You shall go out with joy
Jeremiah		
29	170	And you shall seek me
31	45	Then shall the young girls rejoice
	197	The Lord has said
Lamentations		
3	206	The steadfast love of the Lord
Malachi		
4	116	With healing in his wings
	120	You are the king of glory
Matthew		
3	180	From the distant east
4	204	Seek ye first
6	165	Our Father in heaven
	204	Seek ye first

7	178	Do not judge others
	204	Seek ye first
10	182	God forgave my sin
16	192	If any man will follow
18	191	I was lost but Jesus found me
	204	Seek ye first
21	120	You are the king of glory
25	208	Tell me why do you weep?
26	134	Broken for me
28	182	God forgave my sin

Mark

14	134	Broken for me

Luke

1	28	Mary sang a song
	42	Sing we a song
2	136	Come and go with me
6	178	Do not judge others
11	165	Our Father in heaven
22	134	Broken for me

John

4	108	The well is deep
6	77	I am the bread of life
	120	You are the king of glory
8	21	I will sing, I will sing
12	164	Open our eyes, Lord
13	132	A new commandment
14	71	He is my saviour
	72	He is the way
	95	My peace
	168	You will keep him in perfect peace
	177	Do not be worried

Acts

3	143	Peter and John

Romans

7	209	Thanks be to God
10	109	There's no greater name

1 Corinthians

11	134	Broken for me
12	148	We are one body
15	209	Thanks be to God

2 Corinthians

Chapter	No.	Title
3	130	Where the Spirit of the Lord is
13	137	The grace
	138	The grace of our Lord
	163	May the grace

Galatians

Chapter	No.	Title
5	171	Bring forth the fruit of the Spirit

Ephesians

Chapter	No.	Title
4	133	Bind us together Lord
	148	We are one body

Philippians

Chapter	No.	Title
1	174	Christ in me
	179	For me to live is Christ
2	70	He is Lord
	109	There's no greater name
4	38	Rejoice in the Lord always

Colossians

Chapter	No.	Title
1	209	Thanks be to God
2	107	The fullness of the Godhead

1 Thessalonians

Chapter	No.	Title
4	110	We shall see the Lord in glory

2 Timothy

Chapter	No.	Title
3	152	All scriptures

Hebrews

Chapter	No.	Title
1	120	You are the king of glory
4	209	Thanks be to God
11	211	This world is not my home
12	11	Come and praise the living God

Jude

Chapter	No.	Title
	209	Thanks be to God

Revelation

Chapter	No.	Title
3	150	We will come into his presence
4	19	Holy, holy, holy is the Lord
	121	You are worthy
	150	We will come into his presence
5	19	Holy, holy, holy is the Lord
	121	You are worthy
19	187	I am covered over

FIRST LINE INDEX

A new commandment 132
Abba Father 54
All my heart 151
All over the world 122
All Scriptures 152
All that I am, he made me 169
All the way 65
Alleluia! 1
Alleluia, alleluia 2
Alleluia! alleluia! 3
Alleluia! for the Lord our God 4
Alleluia! going to sing all about it 5
Alleluia, my Father 55
And you shall seek me 170
As water to the thirsty 214

Be still and know 153
Bind us together Lord 133
Break forth and sing for joy 6
Break now the bread of life 154
Bring forth the fruit of the Spirit 171
Broken for me 134
By flowing waters 172
By the waters 173

Christ in me 174
City, O city 135
Clap your hands (I) 7
Clap your hands (II) 8
Cleanse me 175
Come and bless 9
Come and go with me 136
Come and praise him 10
Come and praise the living God 11
Come and praise the Lord our king 66
Come bless the Lord 12
Come, go with me to that land 176
Come into his presence 13
Come Lord Jesus 155
Come sing praises 14
Comes Mary to the grave 67

Day by day 156
Do not be worried 177
Do not judge others 178

Emmanuel, Emmanuel 68

Father we adore you 15
For me to live is Christ 179
From the distant east 180
Fulness of the Godhead, The 107

Give us peace 157
Glorious in majesty 69
Glory Jesus 17
Glory, praise and honour 16
Go, tell it on the mountain 181
God forgave my sin 182
God has spoken 183
God is so good 56
Grace, The 137
Grace of our Lord, The 138
Greatest thing, The 184

Happiness is 185
He is here, he is here 139
He is here 140
He is Lord 70
He is my Saviour 71
He is the way 72
Help me to know you 186
Higher than the hills 73
His name is higher 74
His name is wonderful 75
Holy, holy 18
Holy, holy, holy is the Lord 19
Holy, holy, holy, the Lord God is holy 57
How great is our God 58
How lovely on the mountains 76

I am the bread of life 77
I am covered over 187
I am weak but you are strong 188
I have decided 189
I have made a covenant 59
I want to live for Jesus 190
I was lost but Jesus found me 191

I will enter his gates 20
I will sing, I will sing 21
If any man will follow 192
If I tried 193
If my people 194
I'm in my Father 60
In my life, Lord 195
In the name of Jesus 78
In the presence of your people 22
In your way and in your time 196

Jesus Christ is risen today 79
Jesus Christ, one with God 80
Jesus how lovely you are 81
Jesus I worship you 82
Jesus is Lord alleluia 83
Jesus is the name we worship 84
Jesus, Jesus, Jesus, sweetest name on earth 85
Jesus, Jesus, Jesus your love 86
Jesus, Jesus 87
Jesus' love is very wonderful 88
Jesus my Saviour 89
Jesus, name above all names 90
Jesus stand among us 141
Joy of Jesus 91
Joy of the Lord is my strength, The 23
Jubilate Deo 24
Jubilate everybody 25
Just one touch 92

Kept by the power of God 123
Kum ba yah 158

Let God arise 61
Let me have my way among you 124
Let us break bread together 142
Let us come into his presence 26
Let us praise God together 142
Let us praise the Lord our God 27
Lighten our darkness 159
Lord has said, The 197
Lord Jesus 93
Lord, I want to be a Christian 160
Lord my shepherd, The 198

Make me a channel of your peace 161

Make us worthy, Lord ... 162
Mary sang a song ... 28
May the grace ... 163
Mine are the hands ... 199
My God is so great ... 62
My Lord, he is a-coming soon ... 94
My peace ... 95

Nothing but the love of Jesus ... 96
Now the green blade rises ... 97

O give thanks ... 29
O Holy Spirit breathe on me ... 125
O how good is the Lord ... 30
O praise the Lord ... 31
O sinner man ... 200
O the blood of Jesus ... 98
O the love ... 201
O what a gift ... 99
O when the saints go marching in ... 202
On Calvary's tree ... 100
Open our eyes, Lord ... 164
Our Father in heaven ... 165

Peace is flowing ... 203
Peter and John ... 143
Praise God from whom all blessings flow ... 32
Praise God from whom all blessings flow ... 33
Praise the Lord in his holiness ... 34
Praise the Lord ... 35
Praise you Father ... 36
Precious Jesus ... 101
Prepare the way of the Lord ... 37

Rejoice in the Lord always ... 38
Ruach, Ruach ... 126

See him like a gazelle ... 102
See him lying ... 103
Seek ye first ... 204
Sing a new song ... 39
Sing alleluia ... 104
Sing and rejoice ... 40
Sing his praises ... 41
Sing we a song ... 42
Somebody's knocking at your door ... 105

Sometimes 'Alleluia!' ... 43
Soon and very soon ... 205
Sovereign Lord ... 106
Spirit of God ... 127
Spirit of the living God ... 128
Stand up, clap hands ... 44
Steadfast love of the Lord, The ... 206
Summer has gone, The ... 207

Tell me why do you weep? ... 208
Thank you God for sending Jesus ... 129
Thanks be to God ... 209
Then shall the young girls rejoice ... 45
Therefore the redeemed ... 46
Therefore we lift our hearts ... 47
There's a quiet understanding ... 144
There's a world out there ... 210
There's no greater name ... 109
They say he's wonderful ... 48
This is the day of the Lord ... 145
This is the day ... 146
This world is not my home ... 211
Though the world has forsaken God ... 212
To God be the glory ... 49
To God's loving kindness ... 147
Trust in the Lord ... 213
Turn your eyes ... 166

Unto you O Lord ... 167

We are one body ... 148
We cry, hosanna, Lord ... 50
We have come into his house ... 149
We magnify your name, Lord ... 51
We see the Lord ... 63
We shall see the Lord in glory ... 110
We will come into his presence ... 150
Well is deep, The ... 108
Were you there when they crucified my Lord? ... 215
What a wonderful saviour is Jesus ... 111
What grace ... 112
When I survey ... 113
Where the Spirit of the Lord is ... 130
Wherever I am ... 52
Which way are you choosing? ... 216

Who does Jesus love ... 114
Who is Jesus? ... 115
Who made the mountain ... 64
Wind, Wind ... 131
With healing in his wings ... 116
With my heart I worship you ... 117
Without me ... 118
Wonderful and marvellous ... 119

You are the king of glory ... 120
You are worthy ... 121
You shall go out with joy ... 217
You will keep him in perfect peace ... 168
Your loving kindness ... 53